S1-5
XI
5811

MODERN BUSINESS

A Series of Texts prepared as Part of the

Modern Business Course & Service

Registered Trade Mark
United States and Great Britain
Marca Registrada, M. de F.

ALEXANDER HAMILTON INSTITUTE

PLANT MANAGEMENT

by

John R. Bangs, M.E.

DIRECTOR OF INDUSTRIAL AND PERSONNEL
RELATIONS, THE BUDD COMPANY

Alexander Hamilton Institute, New York

1958 EDITION

*Copyright, 1955, by Alexander Hamilton Institute
Incorporated*

Copyright in Great Britain, 1955, by

Alexander Hamilton Institute Incorporated

All rights reserved, including translation into Scandinavian

Made in U. S. A.

Preface

The progress made in the field of plant management during the few years past has strikingly rivaled that of the previous three decades. From 1903, when Taylor delivered his paper on "Shop Management" before the American Society of Mechanical Engineers, until the First World War broke out in 1914, the development of "scientific management" was slow but thorough. During the war period, the fundamental principles previously built up were widely applied throughout industry. Afterwards, this leaven of information and experience spread rapidly throughout the manufacturing field, and the newer management methods were intensively applied to the operation of American factories.

Today, every large industry, most medium-size plants, and a high percentage of smaller plants have adapted to their organization the principles of modern plant management. Although innumerable variations have been made in the adaptations of management principles to the operation of individual plants, the fundamental principles remain the same.

These principles have received such wide acceptance and universal application that they have come to form the basis of what is known both at home and abroad as the "American" method of manufacturing.

In the present text on "Plant Management," these

principals and their far-reaching significance have been brought out with unusual clearness. To illustrate the application of the basic fundamentals to plant operation, numerous cases from plants noted for their exceptionally efficient management practices have been introduced. The text is also liberally illustrated with helpful charts, drawings and photographs.

The author of this text, John R. Bangs, M.E., has brought to this task not only an extensive practical knowledge from periods of service in various well-known companies, but also an exceptional teaching experience in the field of his subject, having served as Head of the Department of Administrative Engineering, Cornell University.

In 1943, Mr. Bangs became associated with The Budd Company as Director of Industrial and Personnel Relations, and since that time has had unusual insight into the operations of the automobile industry and its suppliers. He has had an opportunity to study plant managers in various situations, and his writing reflects not only a complete concept of the mechanical and organizational problems of modern industry, but also its human side.

The author wishes to express particularly indebtedness to his old Chief, the late Dean Dexter S. Kimball, former dean of the College of Engineering at Cornell University, and to his present Chief, Mr. Edward G. Budd, Jr., President of the Budd Company.

EDITOR-IN-CHIEF

Table of Contents

CHAPTER I
Functions of the Plant Manager

SECTION	PAGE
1. The Fundamental Job of the Plant Manager	1
2. Qualifications of an Executive	1
3. Goals of the Plant Manager	3
4. Formulation of Policies	6
5. Factors in the Selection of Executives	7
6. Seasoned Planning	8
7. Conference Techniques	8
8. The Art of Good Management	9
9. Developing an Organization	10
10. Backing Up Associates	12
11. Defining the Positions Held in an Organization	13
12. Responsibility for Labor Relations	15
13. Leadership	16
14. Morale	17

CHAPTER II
Development of Modern Industry

1. The Industrial World About 1760	20
2. The Industrial Revolution	20
3. Invention of Spinning Machines	21

Contents

SECTION	PAGE
4. The "Mule" of Crompton	22
5. The Factory System	24
6. Other Inventions	24
7. Social Effects	25
8. The Industrial Revolution in the United States	27
9. The Era of Machine Expansion, 1830 to 1887	27
10. The Beginning of Keener Business Competition, 1887–1905	29
11. Advent of a New Technique of Management	29
12. Taylor System of Functional Foremanship	31
13. Modern Influence of Functional Foremanship	32
14. "On the Art of Cutting Metals"	34
15. Taylor Procedures and Techniques	35
16. Leaders of Industrial Management	36

CHAPTER III

Expansion of Industrial Enterprises

1. Trend Toward Large Manufacturing Organizations	37
2. Some Measures of Size	38
3. The Nature of Expansion	39
4. Trends in Mergers	40
5. Reason for Expansion in Size	40
6. Expansion by Aggregation or Accretion	42
7. Horizontal Combinations	42
8. Vertical Combination or Integration	44
9. The Circular Industry	46
10. Chain Combinations	47
11. The Holding-company Method of Combination	48
12. Importance of the Smaller Plant in the Industrial Structure	49

CHAPTER IV

Plant Location

SECTION		PAGE
1.	Factors in Plant Location	51
2.	Raw Materials and Markets	51
3.	Water Power	52
4.	Climate	53
5.	Labor Supply	54
6.	Capital	55
7.	The Effect of Modern Influences	56
8.	Plant Relocations	56
9.	Underlying Reasons for Plant Migration	57
10.	Decentralization	58
11.	Labor Unrest	60
12.	The Product and the Plant Site	61
13.	Locating the Plant	61
14.	Choosing the General Territory	61
15.	Community Selection	62
16.	Size of Community	63
17.	Selecting the Factory Site	63
18.	Method of Selecting a Plant Site	65
19.	Cost Comparisons as a Method of Plant Location	65
20.	Emergency Locations	68

CHAPTER V

Principles of Mass Production

1.	Modern Manufacturing Principles	71
2.	Specialization	71
3.	Specialization in Manufacturing	72
4.	Geographical Specialization	72
5.	Specialization in Marketing	73

SECTION	PAGE
6. Specialization of Callings	73
7. Advantages of Specialization	74
8. Division of Labor	74
9. Other Forms of Division of Labor	76
10. Transfer of Skill	77
11. Transfer of Thought and Intelligence	78
12. Unit Cost and Its Relation to Quantity	79
13. Limiting Influences	80
14. Standardization	81
15. Marketing Standards	82
16. Interchangeability	82
17. Technical Aspects of Standardization, Interchangeability, and Inspection	83
18. International Standards	83
19. National Standards	83
20. Standards Within a Particular Industry	84
21. Standards Within an Individual Factory	84
22. Advantages and Disadvantages of Standardization	86
23. Simplification	87

CHAPTER VI

Line and Staff Control

1. Organization	89
2. Line Organization	89
3. Line and Staff Organization	93
4. Committee Organization	95
5. Executive Committee	96
6. Equipment Committee	97
7. Production Committee	98
8. Committee Principles	98
9. Multiple Management	99
10. Modern Trends in Organization	100

CHAPTER VII

The Works Manager as a Coordinator of Manufacturing Functions

SECTION	PAGE
1. Basic Elements in Organization Practices	102
2. Organization Principles	103
3. Levels of Authority and Responsibility	105
4. Classification of Activities: Assignment of Duties	106
5. Relationships in Organization	108
6. Line Relationships	109
7. Lateral or Cross Relationships	109
8. Functional Staff Relationships	111
9. General Staff Relationships	111
10. Executive Control Through Coordination (Principle of Coordination of Effort)	111
11. Organization Charts and Organization Manuals	112
12. Standard-practice Instructions	115
13. Orders and Reports	116
14. Records of Performance	116
15. Administrative Reports	117
16. Coordination and Control of Functions	117
17. Techniques of Coordination and Control	119
18. Span of Control	120

CHAPTER VIII

Production Planning and Control

1. Control of Production	123
2. Differences in Control Methods Required	123
3. The Need for Accurate Planning	124
4. The Functions of Routing, Scheduling, and Dispatching	124

SECTION	PAGE
5. Handling a Sales Order	125
6. Putting an Order into Production	128
7. Typical Production Control Procedure	128
8. Procedure in Issuing and Accounting for Materials	132
9. Routing and Scheduling of Work	134
10. Mechanisms for Production Control	137
11. Dispatching Work	138
12. Placing the Order on the Planning and Dispatch Boards	138
13. Getting the Work on the Machine	140
14. Completing the Work	141

CHAPTER IX

Purchase, Control and Storing of Materials

1. Purchasing and Its Place in Industry	144
2. Purchasing Policies	144
3. Legal Factors	145
4. Centralized vs. Localized Purchasing	145
5. Place of the Purchasing Department in the Organization	146
6. The Purchasing Agent	147
7. Responsibilities of the Purchasing Department	148
8. Purchase Requisitions	149
9. Requisitions from Several Sources	150
10. Importance of Specifications	150
11. Economies Possible Through Specifications	151
12. Purchase Records	152
13. Receiving and Inspecting	153
14. Stores and Stocks	153
15. Necessity for Storerooms and Stock Rooms	154
16. Ordering Materials for Production	155

Contents

SECTION	PAGE
17. Methods of Regulating Stores and Stocks	156
18. Maximum and Minimum Limits	157
19. Continuous or Perpetual Inventories	158
20. Operating the Finished-parts Storeroom	158
21. Finished-stock Record	159
22. Physical Inventories	160

CHAPTER X

Inspection and Quality Control

1. Control of Quality	162
2. Piece-to-Piece Variation of Parts	163
3. Grouping According to Piece-to-Piece Variations	163
4. Predicting the Proper Limits of a Process	169
5. Departure from Pattern	170
6. Lot Sampling	171
7. The Control Chart	174
8. Use of the Control Chart	177

CHAPTER XI

Plant Buildings, Machinery and Layout

1. Selection of a Suitable Factory	179
2. Methods of Planning and Engineering	180
3. The Use of Process Flow Charts	180
4. Flow Diagrams	182
5. Fundamental Factors in Plant Layout	182
6. Procedures in Developing the Basic Layout	184
7. Analysis of Product	186
8. Selection of Equipment	186
9. Fundamental Methods of Machine Arrangement	186

SECTION	PAGE
10. Process Layout	187
11. Product Layout	188
12. Drawing Board Layouts	192
13. Machine Breakdowns and Repairs	194
14. Heating and Ventilating	195
15. Air Conditioning	196
16. Factory Illumination	197
17. Fire Protection	197

CHAPTER XII

Materials Handling

1. The High Cost of Handling Materials	199
2. Axioms of Materials Handling	199
3. Economies of Efficient Materials Handling	201
4. Methods of Handling	203
5. Industrial-truck Handling	206
6. Detailed Activities Involved in Materials Handling	209
7. Organization for Management of Materials Handling	211
8. Materials-handling Organization in Small Plants	214

CHAPTER XIII

Engineering and Manufacturing Design

1. The Function of the Engineering Department	217
2. Improvement of Products	218
3. Basic Conception of Engineering	219
4. Importance of Methods Engineering	219
5. Tie-in of Product Design with Manufacturing Processes	220
6. Designing Sales Appeal into Manufactured Products	221

Contents

SECTION	PAGE
7. Tooling for Production	222
8. Testing	223
9. Installation	224
10. Supplying Data to Manufacturing Departments	224
11. Use of New Manufacturing Methods and Equipment	226

CHAPTER XIV
Tooling and Automation

1. Definitions	228
2. Determining Tool Requirements	229
3. Tooling	231
4. Tool Control	232
5. Automatic Machinery	233
6. Automation	236
7. Factories that Run Themselves	241

CHAPTER XV
Motion and Time Study

1. Definitions	245
2. Purpose of Motion and Time Study	245
3. Elements of Motion and Time Study	246
4. Preliminary Analysis and Standardization	248
5. Analyzing the Job	249
6. Making Time Studies	250
7. Leveling Factor	255
8. How to Determine a Leveling Factor	260
9. Leveling and Rating Time Studies	261
10. Instruction Cards	262
11. Synthetic Method of Setting Times	263

SECTION	PAGE
12. Use of Formulas in Setting Standard Time	265
13. Ratio-delay Study	265
14. Fatigue	267
15. Motion Economy	267
16. Micromotion Methods	268
17. Elements of Motion or Therbligs	269
18. Methods-Time-Measurement Method	270

CHAPTER XVI
Job Estimating

1. Factors in a Job Estimate	273
2. Cost Estimating	274
3. Elements of a Job Estimate	275
4. Procedures in Job Estimating	280
5. Standards for Job Estimating	281

CHAPTER XVII
Plant Maintenance

1. Preventive Maintenance	283
2. Difference between Maintenance and Repairs	283
3. Maintenance Department Organization	284
4. Kinds of Work Done by the Maintenance Department	284
5. Building Maintenance	285
6. Manufacturing Equipment Maintenance	287
7. Maintenance of Electrical Equipment	287
8. Power Plant Maintenance	287
9. Lighting Maintenance	288
10. Heating, Ventilating and Plumbing Maintenance	288
11. Materials-handling and Transportation Equipment Maintenance	288
12. Service-installations Maintenance	289

Contents

SECTION	PAGE
13. Painting-maintenance Work	289
14. Plant-yard Maintenance	290
15. Maintenance Service	291
16. Maintenance-equipment-and-supplies Storeroom	291
17. Maintenance Records	292

CHAPTER XVIII

Wage Control and Salary Incentive Systems

1. Wage Payment Plans	295
2. Essentials of a Good Wage Payment Plan	296
3. Fundamental Systems of Wage Payment	297
4. Day-wage Plan	298
5. Piecework Systems—Old Method	299
6. Difficulties Encountered Under the Old Piece-rate System	299
7. Objections to Piecework	300
8. Modern Wage Systems	301
9. Combined Piece-rate and Hourly Guarantee, or Modern Piece-rate Plan	302
10. Quality Bonus	303
11. Waste-elimination Bonus	303
12. Other Wage Plans Tried by Companies	303
13. Annual Wage Plans	304
14. Financial Incentive for Supervisors and Executives	306
15. Trends in Industrial Wage Payments	307
16. Success of Incentive Systems Rests with Management	308

CHAPTER XIX

Job Evaluation

1. Nature and Purpose	311
2. Setting Up Wage and Salary Plans	311

Contents

SECTION	PAGE
3. Determination of Relative Value of Jobs	313
4. General Types of Job Measurement	313
5. Job Ranking Plan	313
6. Factor Comparison System	314
7. Factor Point Scoring System	315
8. Classes of Work to Be Covered	318
9. Methods of Making Job Studies	320
10. Applying a Job Evaluation Plan	324

CHAPTER XX
Merit Rating

1. Purpose and Objectives of Merit Rating	328
2. Selecting and Formulating the Rating Factors	329
3. Evaluating the Ratings	331
4. Other Methods of Merit Rating	332

CHAPTER XXI
Personnel Relations

1. The Personnel Department	334
2. Personnel Functions	334
3. Employment	335
4. Movement of Employees within the Organization	336
5. Wage and Salary Control	337
6. Training and Related Activities	338
7. Employee Service	339
8. Financial Aids	340
9. Fringe Benefits	341
10. Safety and Accident Prevention	341
11. Medical Service and Industrial Hygiene	342
12. Employee Records	343

CHAPTER XXII
Labor Relations

SECTION	PAGE
1. Organization of a Labor Relations Department	345
2. Dealing with Unions	346
3. Recognition of Bargaining Unit	346
4. Certification, Holding Elections	347
5. Negotiating the Union Agreement	349
6. Contract Clauses	350
7. Excerpts from Actual Union Contract	350
8. Arbitration	360

CHAPTER XXIII
Modern Industrial Trends

1. The Plant Manager of Today	362
2. Productivity Approved by Labor	362
3. Development of Automatic Machinery	363
4. Increasing Use of Electronic Computers	363
5. Need for Technically Trained People	365
6. Mergers and Consolidation	366
7. The Trend Toward Diversification	366
8. The Prospect for Guaranteed Employment	366
9. Emphasis Being Placed on Executive Development	367
10. Development of the Techniques of Operations Research	367

List of Illustrations

FIGURE		PAGE
1.	Taylor Plan of Functional Foremanship	33
2.	Use of Weighted Factors in Selecting a Plant Site	66
3.	Computations of Delivered-to-customers Cost in Selecting the Location of Cement Mill. Costs Are per Barrel	67
4.	Line Organization	91
5.	Line and Staff Organization	94
6.	Typical Levels of Authority and Responsibility	107
7.	Cross Relationships in an Organization	109
8.	Representative Chart of That Part of the Organization Reporting to the Works Manager	118
9.	Planning Sheet for Controlling Progress of Work	126
10.	Typical Statistical Quality Control Chart	164
11.	Tally of Pieces Sorted into Groups by Operator	166
12.	Pattern from Measuring, Sorting and Counting a Lot of 1,000 Pieces	167
13.	Resultant Variations in All Pieces of a Lot Form a Definite Pattern	169
14.	Pattern of Natural Limits for a Product According to Predictions	171
15.	Distribution Shift from Natural Tolerance Limits	172
16.	Increased Variation-spread Widened in Both Directions	173
17.	Sample Average Falling Outside of the Control Limits	175
18.	Control Chart for Checking Whether the Pattern of the Process Is Repeating Itself or Has Changed	176

List of Illustrations

FIGURE		PAGE
19.	Ranges of Successive Samples Providing a Measure of Process Variations	177
20.	Process Flow Chart	181
21.	Flow Diagram	183
22.	Flow of Work under a Typical Process Layout of Departments	189
23.	Flow of Work under a Typical Product or Straight-line Layout	193

List of Tables

TABLE		PAGE
1.	Performance Rating Table	254
2.	Method of Rating by the Job Rating System	314
3.	Rating of Key Jobs	315
4.	Average of All Committee Members' Ranking of Key Jobs	316
5.	Over-all Committee Estimates of Allocation of Present Hourly Rates	316
6.	Job Factor Point Scoring Plan	317
7.	Typical List of Requirements in Education and Mental Development	318
8.	General Classes of Work Subject to Job Evaluations Methods	320
9.	Methods of Job Study	321
10.	Job Study Check Sheet for Assembling Job Requirements	322–323
11.	Job Grade Substantiating Data	325–326

PLANT MANAGEMENT

CHAPTER I

Functions of the Plant Manager

1. *The fundamental job of the plant manager.* A wide scope of major duties and responsibilities is involved in managing the present-day industrial plant. These obligations are so many that it is impossible for the manager of a plant to handle personally all of them in detail. Consequently, every executive, who successfully heads any of the wide variety of manufacturing companies which are in operation today, first divides his organization into a number of units. He then selects men to direct the work of these respective units, and places upon their shoulders the burden of immediate operation.

Each of these division heads, in turn, subdivides his unit of the enterprise in a similar way. Finally, a level in the organization is reached where the directional attention needed to get the actual work done is within the scope and powers of individuals who can give personal attention to securing the desired productive results.

2. *Qualifications of an executive.* An excellent approach to the qualities needed by an executive are the

following characteristics of a good executive outlined by Donald A. Laird. This list of characteristics was compiled after a rather thorough check with industrial executives throughout American industry.

Qualities of a Good Executive

(a) A good executive has the capacity, mental, physical, or what-you-will of impressing others as having oceans of confidence in himself.

(b) Has marked judgment of men so that those he has selected turn out to be superior in the jobs and posts to which he has assigned them.

(c) His judgment of events is such that he has been able to anticipate future changes and developments.

(d) Has an innate and active desire to plan and organize the work of others.

(e) Has a clear and fearless desire to meet other men openly.

(f) Has an inspirational quality, persuasive or forceful, or both, that brings others to his viewpoint and keeps them working toward a common goal.

(g) Has a continued disposition to seek responsibility, to make decisions and to stand by them in the face of odds.

(h) Usually sure enough of himself and his job to size up situations, to plan courses of action and put them into operation in what to many men would seem the twinkling of an eye. (This gives him a claim on leadership in any group.)

Functions of the Plant Manager

(i) Demonstrates a liking and a capacity for doing a good job of direct person-to-person leadership (rather than one addicted to sitting back and striving to get things done by others through undercover, impersonal and subtle maneuvers).

(j) Openly ready to accept responsibility for blunders without a predilection for buck passing.

(k) Remarkably free from prejudice.

(l) Good mixer.

(m) Omnivorous reader.

(n) Wants others to understand his reasons for his acts.

(o) Openly invites suggestions from others, but is equally downright in doing as he likes about them.

(p) He always wants the facts and gets them.

(q) He is consistent in his attitude toward events and toward persons.

(r) He knows what he wants and can make these wants clear to others.

(s) Has the precious quality of being able to criticize without antagonizing his fellows.

(t) He delegates responsibility without fear that in so doing he is lessening his own importance.

(u) He is, all in all, a direct and fearless realist.

3. *Goals of the plant manager.* Without goals, no effort of management can be so applied as to accomplish the greatest success. Every business or industrial executive who guides his enterprise to the highest attain-

ments sets in advance for each project a definite objective, or ultimate attainable point, at which he wishes to arrive.

A well-defined goal can be achieved most readily if the manager directs all his energies along the definite line or path worked out, and discards all means which will be of no aid in the program. He thus avoids going off the path and conserves all his energies for getting to the real goal. His associates, moreover, are better able to understand his plans, and develop their own procedures toward the same end.

Among the goals of an executive, the following may be included:

I *Production*
   (a) Simplification of product design and standardization in products to introduce mass production wherever possible.
   (b) Greater efficiency in manufacturing the company's products.
   (c) An excellently functioning system of production planning and control.
   (d) Control over the quality of products.
   (e) A well-maintained plant.
   (f) Introduction of cost-saving machinery through equipment studies.
   (g) Improvements of plant layout to gain the greatest advantages from straight-line production.
   (h) Reduction of costs through improved materials-handling methods and equipment.

Functions of the Plant Manager

(i) Economy and balanced control in purchasing and storing.

II *Marketing*

(a) Steadily widening the company's markets through promotion of present products.

(b) Product improvement and adaptation to reach new customers with current products.

(c) Expanding the markets through the development of new products.

(d) Building up a capable, alert and successful sales force.

III *Financial*

(a) Maintaining the company on a profit-paying basis at all times.

(b) Building adequate reserves for business development and for equipment replacements and emergencies.

(c) Financing the business through earnings rather than borrowing.

IV Personnel

(a) High morale and a spirit of cooperation and progress among executives, department heads, supervisors, foremen and workers.

(b) Good wage policies to remunerate workers in conformity with their actual economic contributions to the enterprise.

(c) Acceptable and fair plans for rewarding the more efficient workers with extra earnings for increased output.

(d) Fair evaluation of jobs to provide pay bases commensurate with each job's requirements and demands.

(e) A fair means of rating the individual merits of workers according to the manner in which they fulfill their responsibilities and perform their tasks.

(f) Good working conditions, highly developed safety methods, and other factors of benefit to employees.

(g) Fair dealings on both sides—labor and management—on all debatable points to keep the plant free from slowdowns, sitdowns, strikes and all other labor disturbances.

4. *Formulation of policies.* Policy formulation is the function of the plant manager, but it requires the aid and information which can best be supplied only by the operating and staff men. Policies should be set for each major division of activities as, for example, the following:

(a) The company aims to concentrate on certain specified products.

(b) It will carry on research to improve these products constantly.

(c) It will set up certain standards of quality and maintain them by quality control.

(d) It will add to its line to keep abreast of markets as they develop, but will base its plans on sound market analysis.

Functions of the Plant Manager

(e) Time standards will be set wherever feasible on jobs, and these standards will be established by competent time-study men.
(f) Base wage rates will be those of the community, with incentive factors added for extra accomplishment.
(g) A standard cost system will be used to control manufacturing expenditures.
(h) Organized production planning and control will be carried on to set and maintain definite, efficient manufacturing procedures, schedules and delivery dates.

When such basic policies are established, the department heads have the means of knowing the fundamentals under which the company operates. They are thus able to follow a common pattern in their own activities, and in relation to the work of other departments. Furthermore, under established policies, employees are not plagued with uncertainties as to job security, fair pay, ethical and considerate treatment, and other factors in their relations with the company.

5. *Factors in the selection of executives.* R. E. Gillmor, President of the Sperry Corporation points out that the slow progress which has been made in the art of management is due to the inability to separate variables and to prove principles by measurement. He calls attention to the fact that executives are usually selected on the basis of trial and error rather than on qualifications in education and training.

As Mr. Gillmor states, "Such training as is given to executives is usually applied at the lower levels, the result often being to make the lower levels critical of their seniors when they find that the senior does not practice the precepts which have been taught to the junior."

6. *Seasoned planning.* Many of the problems of the industrial plant do not lend themselves to ready or rapid solution. Seasoned thinking is necessary to work them out. Similarly, new ideas and suggestions usually require considerable deliberation before they can be put into operation. An effective plan followed by some executives is to develop the methods proposed in written form but, except in emergency, not to apply them immediately. Instead, the suggestions are put away for a time until, when picked up again, they can be reviewed apart from the immediate circumstances under which they were prepared.

If these suggestions then seem sound, logical, complete and effective, they are likely to work and bring about the desired results. Any flaws, shortcomings or inefficiencies usually will show up clearly during such a review, and these can be corrected before applying the plan.

7. *Conference techniques.* It is frequently necessary to bring department heads together for conferences on plans and procedures. The plant manager is responsible for a wide range of industrial activities, and many of the plans and steps for putting them into effect must be

Functions of the Plant Manager

a composite of the recommendations of the men who head the various units of the company.

Conferences are intended to bring out the pertinent facts of the particular subjects under discussions, so that result-producing decisions can be reached and put into effect. After the manager states the problem which is up for consideration, and blocks out the situation in its apparent form, he should then open the way for the contribution of facts within the knowledge of his conferees. In many cases, moreover, it is good practice to have the men concerned with the projects introduce the subjects themselves, with their explanations and recommendations of procedures to be followed. The manager can then open the way for full discussion, reserving his own ideas or summary until the subject has been thoroughly threshed out.

8. *The art of good management.* The art of good management is to create an organization which will develop to its highest point the initiative of individuals, consistent with an orderly process and cohesiveness of purpose.

Management is an art, not a science. Hence, its forms express the personality and color of one man—the top executive. Through his choices, his example, and his instructions, the executive creates an extension of himself throughout the organization. From this it follows that there is no single, royal road to building a good organization.

Take the question of whether the top executive

should dominate and supervise every detail. That depends partly on his own character and partly on the ability of the immediate subleaders. It is best if the executive can free himself from daily routine, and spend his time in supervising and in scanning the field for improvements. He should take care, however, that he does not get so far out of touch with the daily occurrences in the organization that his judgments become warped or abstract.

The question also may be asked as to whether there should be a single "number two" man, or whether there should be a group of equally important and trusted executives at the next level of authority? Should the "number one" be a lonely figure, or should he be the leader of an equal group, "primus inter pares"? These are not questions of good or bad; they are matters of personality. Many solutions can work with good results if the personality factors are allowed to have effective play.

Promotions from within are a favorite way of stimulating the members of an organization to do better work in the hope of achieving advancement. Within broad limits, this is a wise policy.

9. *Developing an organization.* In building up an organization of capable associates, the plant manager, as far as possible, should not merely open the way for progress in all departments of the company. He should also insist that his associates pioneer in new ideas, think their way through most of their problems, and con-

Functions of the Plant Manager

stantly endeavor to upgrade the work of their departments.

The plant manager should be on his guard against participating directly in the work of the different departments, except in emergencies, or when specially called upon for needed help. Department heads should be discouraged from coming to the manager for a ruling or opinion on the details of their activities. Men do not grow by leaning on their executive directors.

The best policy for a manager is to let his department heads work out their own plans and programs. His primary interest should be in seeing that these plans fit in with and contribute to the progress of the enterprise as a whole, and that they have constructive effects on the personnel of the entire organization. The direct participation of the manager in all decisions and actions makes the company a one-man-idea organization. The best results are obtained by securing the suggestions and by drawing upon the experience of other members of the company who also are able thinkers and planners.

Plant managers who are doing the more advanced thinking often give their associates opportunity to learn by exploring the possibilities of some important new plan or project, making their own decisions, and following through by putting the plan into action. If the particular plan succeeds, the associate develops increased confidence in his ability. Such pioneering experience thus contributes to his growth, so that he is eventually able to take some of the burdens from the manager's shoulders.

If the plan fails, the associate still benefits from the experience. He is encouraged by the fact that he had a fair chance to try out his ideas; he learns why and how the proposition did not work; he profits by seeing where he made his mistakes. His experience thus gears him up to make good on his next proposal. It increases his determination to show that he can develop something on a new attempt that will actually be successful.

10. *Backing up associates.* One of the duties of the top executive is to accept ultimate responsibility for the results of measures taken by his associates in connection with the development of new plans. It is especially his duty to back them up when, in spite of intelligent and earnest effort, they end in failure. Where the steps taken on some important project involve the possibility of failure as well as the prospect of success, the associate in immediate charge has a major problem on his hands. Within the scope of his job, he is taking a long chance.

Naturally, the associate calls upon the top executive to weigh the problem and to advise on taking the risk. The top executive, in evaluating the possibilities from the standpoint of other phases of the business, and in measuring the effects of failure as well as of success, takes a certain responsibility upon himself. To the top executive, failure of the plan is usually a relatively minor matter in his scope of responsibilities. To the associate concerned, failure is of major importance. A discerning executive in such cases will share the blame for the failure.

Among the top executive's responsibilities is that of clearing the way for the free action of his associates' plans when they have been found satisfactory, sound, and worth while carrying through. In putting a plan into effect, a department head often finds it necessary to arrange for coordinate steps or actions to be taken by some other departments, and for the use of the facilities of these other departments. Conferences may be required among a number of departments to draw up interconnected plans. Conflicts and friction between departments must be prevented, and teamwork developed, so that the required concerted action can be brought about. These are problems which are difficult to solve satisfactorily without the aid of the top executive.

11. *Defining the positions held in an organization.* A highly important matter in any industrial enterprise is that of defining the functions of the various positions held. While some progress has been made in this respect, especially through job evaluations studies and the development of job specifications at the worker level, few companies have taken adequate constructive steps along this line in connection with the higher positions. What, for example, is the job of a vice-president or a superintendent?

R. E. Gillmor, who has had a long experience in

organizational development, points out that, "No man can make full and effective use of his talent and energy unless he knows for what he is responsible, to whom he is responsible, and how he is to be judged. Absence of adherence to such principles also leads to continual changes in organization structure. In far too many cases, the structure is designed for the individuals who are available. The proper way, of course, is to design the organization structure in accordance with sound principles and choose the individuals to fit the structure."

This should not be taken, however, as justification for a blind adherence to an intensified organizational structure as a preventive of duplicated effort, conflicting effort and diverted effort. An organization chart, at any one time, is static, while the typical organization manual, which defines the duties and responsibilities of positions on such a chart, merely serves in many cases to block out the fields of activity of the various positions.

Recognizing the importance of using the talents of the managerial group to the best over-all advantage, some companies pay less attention to charts and manuals, and more to individual qualifications. When a problem of unusual nature arises, they prefer to pick the man best fitted to handle the task and forget about organizational lines.

Most problems, however, are confined to one department or another, and are consequently solved by the

Functions of the Plant Manager

respective department heads in their usual line of duties. Even when exceptional problems arise and the need for flexibility of organization is recognized, it is still possible to pick special men for special jobs without interfering with the authority and field of action of any department heads.

12. *Responsibility for labor relations.* The plant manager cannot help regarding his plant as a large, complicated machine consisting of a combination of equipment and workers brought together to convert materials into salable goods for a waiting market. His job, as he sees it, is to integrate all these varied manufacturing elements into an effective and correctly functioning mechanism.

Workers, on the other hand, look upon their jobs not merely as a means of livelihood and an opportunity to work at their chosen vocations, but also as really a major part of their lives. In most cases, workers who have good employment, good pay and considerate employers, are well-satisfied with their company connections, and their families share in this satisfaction. While they expect good pay and good working conditions, they also value individual recognition and opportunities to demonstrate their skill and ability.

Many executives who are among the leaders in developing advanced practices in the personnel field, are of the opinion that practically half of the plant manager's job has to do with labor relations, ranking in importance with efficiency of production, his other major responsibility. When workers receive the right treatment from a management that they trust, it is usually the case that they take personal interest not only in their work, but also in the progress of the company, and need no urge to make good in their respective jobs.

13. *Leadership.* No matter how well organized and manned a company may be, it takes real leadership to bring out the best qualities of the supervisory and working force, and to secure the most satisfactory results in the operation of the company. Some executives take naturally to leadership. They have the qualifications which inspire their associates with zeal for their work, loyalty to the organization, and spontaneous cooperation with those for whom they work. Other executives acquire leadership through conscious effort.

The chief characteristic of leadership is that the followers are willing to do what the leader tells them, blindly, zealously, enthusiastically, and often at the risk of their own injury, or sometimes even of their lives.

It is difficult to develop the members of a supervisory staff into fundamentally capable leaders, probably because most men who are leaders themselves do not know exactly how they get response and action from their own associates. They are consequently at a loss as to how to train others in the strengthening and in the application of potential leadership characteristics.

A. Cohen, of London, England, an industrial engineer with wide consulting experience in a number of continental organizations, has presented pertinent in-

Functions of the Plant Manager

formation of a constructive nature on the subject of leadership. He lists the qualities of a leader as follows:

(a) Habits and attitudes of a constructive nature.
(b) Insight into members of his group and into himself.
(c) Clear, logical thinking, and submitting impulsive, emotional or habitual urges to this thinking.
(d) Physical and mental health.
(e) Personality and character.

The fact that some object is achieved does not necessarily indicate good leadership. Circumstances and the normal action of those carrying on some undertaking may make accomplishment a foregone conclusion.

As stated by Mr. Cohen, a successful leader does the following:

(a) Determines the purpose.
(b) Creates the apparatus for fulfilling the purpose.
(c) Causes the members of his organization to use the apparatus.

14. *Morale.* A plant manager's success depends to a large extent on the maintenance of the morale of the working force at a high level. Lansburgh and Spriegel, in discussing the subject of morale in their text on *Industrial Management,* list the factors which stimulate morale, and those which cause it to break down, as follows:

I Stimuli of morale:
  (a) Clearly defined responsibilities.
  (b) An adequate supervisory force.
  (c) Proper selection and promotion of personnel.
  (d) Dynamic leadership.
II Dangers causing a breakdown of morale:
  (a) Too fine a division of authority and responsibility.
  (b) Too many supervisors.
  (c) Improper selection of personnel for new or expanded duties:
    (1) Do not let seniority rule.
    (2) Do not bring in outsiders. Rather re-layout the organization to use present supervisors.
  (d) Over-reliance on organization charts.
  (e) Too few real executives.

Review

What method does a successful plant manager use to prevent himself from being burdened with too many details?

Name some of the qualifications needed by a top executive.

Why should a plant manager have well-defined goals, and what are some of the goals that he might endeavor to achieve?

Why is it important to establish definite policies and what should be the basic characteristics of such policies?

What is the advantage of postponing consideration of suggestions and proposed plans?

Functions of the Plant Manager

How should conferences be conducted so as to produce the best results?

Name some methods a plant manager might use to develop his subordinates.

Give an instance when it might be wiser to subordinate organization charts and manuals to individual qualifications.

What are a plant manager's two major responsibilities?

What are some of the qualities which make for leadership?

NOTE: The review at the end of each chapter is for the personal convenience of the reader in testing his understanding of the chapter. It is not necessary or desirable for the subscriber to submit written answers to the Institute except in a case where he may be uncertain as to his grasp of the subject under consideration.

CHAPTER II

Development of Modern Industry

1. *The industrial world about 1760.* The actual beginning of our present-day industrial era occurred about 1760. Up to that time, industry was very simply set up. Production was carried on by handicraft workers who were unorganized and without legal protection, toiling in their homes. There were textile machines operated by foot power; crude water wheels; horse-drawn vehicles for transportation. These were the conditions existing when there suddenly occurred a series of dramatic events that have not, even to this day, ceased to make themselves felt.

2. *The Industrial Revolution.* These events, which made up what is know as the Industrial Revolution, included the advent of the inventor; epoch-making machines in spinning and weaving; economic, social and political upheavals; and the beginnings of mass production. Thus, about 1760, was born the machine era.

For hundreds of years, England's most staple industry was the production of woolen goods. By 1760, however, cotton had begun to challenge this wool monopoly. The device known as the flying shuttle, which was

Development of Modern Industry

invented as early as 1733 by John Kay, a weaver of Bury, to overcome certain difficulties in weaving, had become generally accepted by the weaving fraternity by 1760. A shortage of yarn followed, since six to eight spinners were required to supply one weaver. The result was that England, especially since she was pressed for cotton cloth through war and export trade, offered prizes of 50 pounds and 25 pounds for the best and second best improvement in the construction of spinning machines.

3. *Invention of spinning machines.* The response to these offers was almost instantaneous; three machines, those of Highs, Hargreaves and Arkwright, appeared in rapid succession. The first of these, a multiple spinning wheel, was invented by Thomas Highs in 1764. In 1767, this invention was modified and improved by James Hargreaves, who produced a machine which would operate eight spindles simultaneously. This machine he called the "Spinning Jenny" in honor, as it is claimed, of his daughter Jane. Spinners, who saw in this machine a fertile cause for future unemployment, entered Hargreaves' home and destroyed his machine.

Hargreaves then moved to Nottingham where he enlisted the cooperation of additional capital. Although workers, cotton manufacturers, and especially wool manufacturers continued hostile to the invention, he built several good spinning jennies. The yarn produced by this machine, however, was not sufficiently strong to be used for warp, the thread that extends lengthwise in the weave. It could be used only for weft, which is carried across the warp by the shuttle.

A spinning machine based on a different principle was devised shortly afterwards, however, to provide a stronger yarn for the warp. This invention used rollers to draw out the cotton, and spindles to twist the thread. Richard Arkwright, a barber of Bolton, and a shrewd organizer of men, money and materials, hired one Kay, a former assistant of Highs, to build for him a secret model. From this crude beginning was developed a quite satisfactory machine. This would run thread to any degree of fineness, giving the weavers a plentiful supply of warp as well as woof (weft). Its product was called water twist, because water was used as motor power for driving the machine.

Arkwright's first patent was granted in 1769. Then, after numerous litigations, he was granted a second patent in 1775, which contained ten claims covering a complete machine layout for carding and roving cotton.

Building many mills, and otherwise expanding his interests by granting licenses for the use of his machinery, Arkwright became involved in many legal suits, with the final result that his patents were declared invalid. Such a result would have crushed many a strong man, but Arkwright's social and business standing was so strong that he sailed right on. A year later he was knighted, and at his death left a large fortune.

4. *The "Mule" of Crompton.* One defect of Arkwright's roller was that it exerted too much pressure

Development of Modern Industry

upon the thread, making the spinning of a real fine yarn impossible. In 1779, Samuel Crompton, a spinner, combined the good features of the previous machines, and invented what was known as a mule—a hybrid or cross of several machines. As a result, thread and cotton cloth were so cheapened that parliament rescinded its former restrictive acts in favor of wool manufactures, and fully approved of the use of pure cotton goods, provided that they were of English manufacture.

In 1774, the English consumption of cotton goods was 4,000,000 pounds; in 1806, it had risen to 56,000,000 pounds. During the period between these years, the cotton textile industry was again thrown out of balance. As the result of Compton's invention, the weavers had more thread and yarn than their machinery could handle.

In 1785, however, an English clergyman by the name of Cartwright, who was a true novice in this field of invention, produced the power loom. Despite the usual resistance of the hand workers, the machine became fully accepted by 1800. The adoption of the power loom, together with the advent of the calico printing machine and the improvements in the steam engine, completed the mechanization of the textile industry. This concentrated production in the factory and gave rise to modern capitalism.

The machines of Hargreaves, Arkwright, Crompton and Cartwright, are known historically as the four great inventions. The technological changes in manufacturing, and the social, economic and political upheavals which followed these inventions comprised the Industrial Revolution.

5. *The factory system.* The term "factory system" refers to the movement originated by Arkwright and his predecessors, which led to the establishment of buildings which housed expensive machinery far beyond the capital of the average worker. It led to a separation of the worker from his production tools; it gave rise to capitalism; and it brought about sweeping changes in economic and social conditions. The terms "manufacturing system and factory system" still apply to the mass production of today.

6. *Other inventions.* The principle of transfer of skill from men to machines, once it was understood, extended its influence to many fields. Of particular note were the many important inventions in the machine tool field. One of these inventions was Wilkinson's boring machine in 1775 for boring the cylinders of Watt's steam engine. Other inventions of this kind were the slide rest lathe, the planer, the steam hammer and other machine tools which were primarily necessary in the building of textile machines. In fact, these machines to build machines made the present era a possibility. They are rightfully known as the "master tools of industry."

In 1785, James Watt improved the steam engine to such an extent that it could be harnessed to textile machinery. This made it possible for factories, formerly

Development of Modern Industry

dependent upon water, to be moved to locations which were more suitable for manufacturing. As the result of these developments, manufacturing capacity began to outstrip the cotton supply in the United States.

In 1792, however, Eli Whitney came to the rescue by inventing the cotton gin. This invention made it possible for British manufacturers to obtain again all the American cotton which they could use. Thus came the great combination: suitable machines, adequate manufacturing capacities harnessed with motive power, and sufficient raw materials.

Paralleling and a distinct part of this development in manufacturing came the extension of the canal system, the locomotive of Stephenson, the production of iron rails in Coalbrookdale, and the greater accessibility of coal through the improvement of mine pumping machinery. All of these helped to usher in the dawn of rapid transportation as an aid to distributing the products of manufacture.

7. *Social effects.* Shaken out of its comfortable medieval existence, England was thrown into turmoil by the development of the factory system. The effects were far-reaching and complex. Thousands of workers found that their hand-tools of production were no longer adequate. Even with the utmost perseverance, they were unable to compete with the new machines. In order to earn a living, these workers were forced to leave their farms, shops and cottages and move into towns where they could get jobs in factories.

This created a new problem, since there were no laws nor restraints, either legal or moral, having to do with the proper treatment of labor. Employers set their own terms which labor was compelled to take, and degradation of labor overtook all who sought to toil. Unbelievable working conditions arose.

As a result, England was faced with the task of correcting this situation. The first step was to get laws enacted which would improve labor conditions in the factories. The battle for legal regulation was led by such men as Robert Owen, Richard Oestler and Sir Robert Peel, and in 1802 the first modern factory act was put into effect.

This act reduced the hours of labor of children to 72 per week, provided them with elementary instruction, caused factories to be made more sanitary, and set a penalty of not more than £5 or less than 48 shillings for all who violated the act. In 1800, at the New Lanark Mills, Robert Owen demonstrated that good working and living conditions were desirable, since they enabled his mills to operate at a greater profit. He thus began the work which led to the adoption of the modern personnel policies.

Following the enactment of legislation in behalf of labor, a movement was started toward the organization of labor for its further protection, and unions sprang into existence. Another movement which got under way was that of providing vocational education. This was brought into being by the collapse of the old

Development of Modern Industry

apprenticeship systems and by the development of entirely new problems in the training of factory personnel. The corrective movements, however, like all regulatory influences, were very slow in showing results.

8. *The Industrial Revolution in the United States.* Quick to see the advantages of their newly invented machines, England prohibited their exportation. The colonies of America, however, were not long deprived of their use. About 1790, Samuel Slater, a young Englishman who was skilled in constructing Arkwright machines, built several of them for Almy and Brown, and started the first textile factory in Pawtucket, Rhode Island. This factory, known as the Slater Mill, was a pronounced success, and was given the credit for pioneering the introduction of these new machines in America. Thus, Samuel Slater may aptly be called the "father of American manufacturers."

9. *The era of machine expansion, 1830 to 1887.* During and following the days of Samuel Slater, machine methods and the factory system grew rapidly in America, with fast progress also being made in the means of transportation. This was an age of great mechanical expansion. Following one after another in rapid succession came the automatic mower, the telegraph, the sewing machine, the sole-sewing machine, the Bessemer process in making steel, and many other inventions of lesser importance.

Introduced in 1833, McCormick's "automatic mower" greatly reduced the costs of grain production and stimulated a new technique in agriculture. The electric telegraph of Samuel Morse, perfected in 1838, revolutionized communication, while Elias Howe's invention of the sewing machine in 1845 made possible large scale production of clothing. In England, Sir Henry Bessemer perfected his famous Bessemer process for making steel in 1859, thus laying the foundation for the remarkable growth of steel which was to follow.

Paralleling this remarkable series of mechanical inventions was the growth of American transportation facilities. After the advent of railway systems, industry and population grew particularly fast. In fact, from 1840 to 1860, the period of most active railroad building, the rate of increase in the population of the United States was the highest in the country's history.

The Baltimore and Ohio, and the Mohawk and Hudson railroads were founded shortly after 1830, pioneering to a large extent the development of railroad transportation; while the Reading Railway of Pennsylvania was the first to demonstrate that coal could be transported as cheaply by land as by water. In 1854, the completion of a road from Buffalo to Pittsburgh opened up a new era of prosperity for that section of the country.

After an interruption in railroad expansion as the result of the Civil War, the railroads began the process of linking the Eastern cities through the Alleghenies to the Middle West, and finally over the Rockies to the Pacific Coast. The construction of the Union Pacific

Development of Modern Industry

had a particularly beneficial influence upon many phases of manufacturing, and brought about unusual prosperity. Meanwhile, the South, too, made comparable progress in railroad development.

10. *The beginning of keener business competition, 1887–1905.* During the period from 1887 to 1905, the railroads ceased to grow at their former rate, since lines had been extended to every part of the country. As a result, there was a slower development of new markets, and it became necessary to give more careful study to existing markets. Thus, intensive business competition began to develop, with manufacturers seeking more efficient methods of controlling production and of reducing costs.

In 1903, Frederick W. Taylor presented before the American Society of Mechanical Engineers his historic paper on *Shop Management*, which crystallized the scientific principles that industry so badly needed. Associated with him were men like Gantt, Emerson, Barth and Gilbreth, a group which spread the gospel of better management to many fields of endeavor.

11. *Advent of a new technique of management.* The individual work of no person has had such a great influence on the operation of American industrial plants as that of Frederick Winslow Taylor. Taylor had prepared to enter Harvard University for study of the law, but the impairment of his vision compelled him to forego a career which involved much reading.

At the age of eighteen years, Taylor began apprenticeship as machinist and pattern marker in a small shop in Philadelphia. Having completed that training, he sought a position at the Midvale Steel Company. Because business was not good and skilled labor was not in demand, he had to be satisfied to start with a yard laborer's job. Soon afterwards, however, he was made a gang boss—an assistant foreman—supervising a group of men working chiefly on lathes. Then, at the young age of 26, he became chief engineer of the plant.

Almost immediately, Taylor plunged into the difficulties of management. The output was low, but since he had been a worker among workers of that day, he knew that this low output was not merely the result of the unconscious adoption of the normal shop pace, but that it also resulted from deliberate systematic soldiering. It was natural for him at first to imitate the methods of foremen under whom he had worked. Consequently, he attempted to force production by driving the workers, the method of foremanship then customary. A bitter fight with his men resulted.

This highly unsatisfactory state of affairs caused Taylor to study the whole situation thoroughly. He decided that, under the circumstances, the attitude of the workers was not unnatural—perhaps not unreasonable—and that management was chiefly at fault. He found that management's concept of a proper day's work was what a foreman could *drive* workers to do, and that the workers' conception was how little they could do and hold their jobs. He then came to the conclusion that it

Development of Modern Industry

was management's business to *know* what was a proper day's work, and that the only way to know would be by research and experiment.

The result was that Taylor requested and secured permission to conduct "some experiments." Almost immediately, these experiments yielded results in the nature of measured procedures and possibilities of work which put supervision and management of his gang, and later of the entire shop, on a *factual* basis. The body of interlocking procedures which resulted from these investigations came to be known as the "Taylor System," while the name "Scientific Management" was given to the doctrine and principles later derived from these procedures.

12. *Taylor system of functional foremanship.* In the process of his investigations, Taylor made an analysis of the duties of a first-class foreman as found in the organization of his day. He found that such a foreman must be able to do the following:

- (a) Be a good machinist.
- (b) Be able to read drawings readily.
- (c) Plan the work of his department.
- (d) See that each man keeps his machine clean and in good order.
- (e) See that each man turns out work of the proper quality.
- (f) See that the men work steadily and fast.
- (g) See that the work flows through the work centers in the proper sequence.

(h) In a general way, supervise time keeping and rate setting.

(i) Maintain discipline and adjust wages.

While it was evident that men with these various aptitudes would make valuable foremen, the fact remained that such men could rarely be found. Taylor therefore devised the plan of having "functional" rather than all-around foremen. Each of the eight functions of the all-around foreman was assigned to a different man, and the work of planning the operations was changed from the shop to the office. Taylor outlined these fields as shown in Figure 1.

The time and cost clerk, instruction card clerk, and route clerk attended to the mental and clerical functions of production, while the gang boss, speed boss, repair boss and inspector looked after the actual production in the shop. A disciplinarian was appointed to look after the disciplinary functions of the whole plant. The duties of the gang boss were to see that work and materials were moved efficiently from machine to machine. The speed boss served as an instructor to the workmen, while the repair boss and the inspector performed the duties indicated by their titles.

13. *Modern influence of functional foremanship.* Functional foremanship as Taylor devised it was not widely adopted. Its success in industry was limited and, as a "system," it seems to have disappeared almost entirely from today's industrial scene. Nevertheless, the principle of functionalization has been applied on a

Development of Modern Industry

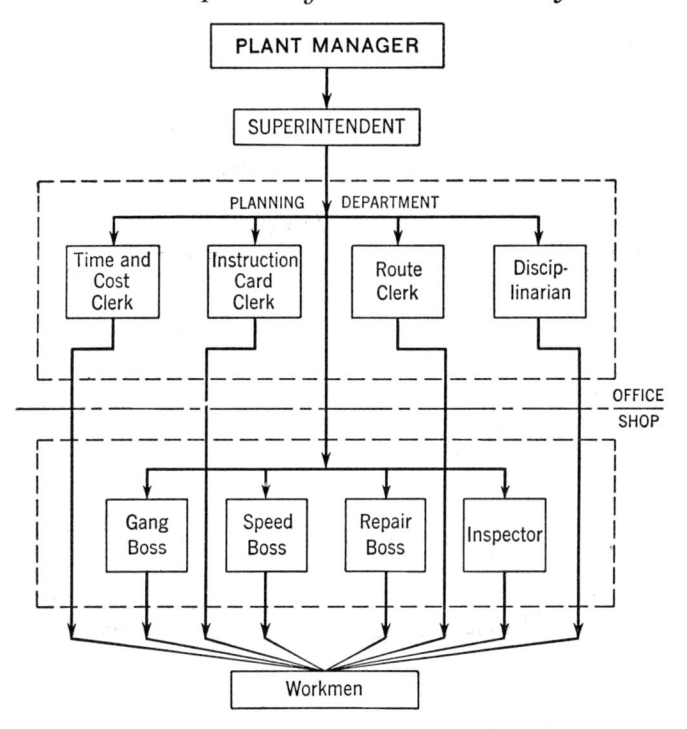

FIGURE 1—TAYLOR PLAN OF FUNCTIONAL FOREMANSHIP

wide scale in industry. Today's functional specialists, however, have little or no authority to carry out their ideas, whereas Taylor's functional foremen combined expertness in a particular line with authority to act. Therein seems to have been the weakness of the system, because too many bosses created confusion.

The influence of functional foremanship may be seen, however, by examining any modern organization chart. Such a chart will reveal the following:

(a) The gang boss is now the set-up man on machines.

(b) The speed boss is the foreman or assistant responsible for getting the work out on time.

(c) The repair boss has grown into the repair department.

(d) The inspector has expanded into the inspection organization.

(e) The time and cost clerk are members of the accounting and cost departments.

(f) The instruction and route clerks, perhaps under varying names, carry on many important functions in the planning department.

(g) The disciplinarian, strange as it may seem, is now the modern department of personnel relations.

14. *"On the Art of Cutting Metals."* In his investigations, Taylor found that management had no idea how fast machines should be run, or how metal should be cut. He started a research program that eventually extended over a period of twenty-six years, during which time he spent between $150,000 and $200,000 in cutting up more than 800,000 pounds of steel and iron under experimental conditions. His researches were published under the title of "On the Art of Cutting Metals" in *Mechanical Engineering,* 1906.

Associated with Taylor were Carl Barth, a mathematician, and Maunsel White, a metallurgist. Barth greatly aided in simplifying the masses of data gath-

Development of Modern Industry

ered, while out of the Taylor-White association came the first high speed steel.

15. *Taylor procedures and techniques.* Although it is true that the Taylor system as a "system" was never widely adopted in its original details, Taylor's procedures and techniques literally changed the make-up of American factories. Among these procedures may be listed the following:

- (a) Time study.
- (b) Functional foremanship.
- (c) Standardization of tools and machines.
- (d) The planning department.
- (e) The "exception principle" in management.
- (f) The use of slide rules for metal cutting.
- (g) Instruction cards for workmen.
- (h) The task idea in management, accompanied by a large bonus for the successful performance of the task.
- (i) The "differential piece rate."
- (j) Mnemonic systems for classification in tool rooms, storerooms and stock rooms.
- (k) Stores control system and pre-apportioning of materials to jobs.
- (l) The work routing system and the preparation of operation and route sheets.
- (m) Modern systems for cost keeping and cost accounting.

Of the foregoing thirteen procedures, only three failed to stand the test of time. These were functional foremanship, the use of metal cutting slide rules, and the differential piece rate. All the others served as a basis for the development of the management techniques and procedures of the present day.

16. *Leaders of industrial management.* Four men are generally acknowledged as having been the pioneers in the development of industrial management. First and foremost was Taylor himself. Two others, Henry Lawrence Gantt and Frank Bunker Gilbreth, were his close associates. A fourth, Harrington Emerson, was widely known for his twelve principles of efficiency and his work for the Santa Fe Railroad.

Review

Describe industrial conditions prior to 1760.

What was the Industrial Revolution?

What are known historically as the four great inventions and who were the inventors?

Describe the social effects of the introduction of the factory system?

Name three movements which took place in behalf of labor after the beginning of the Industrial Revolution.

Who is entitled to be called the "father of American manufacturers" and why?

What were the outstanding features of the era of machine expansion from 1830 to 1887?

What was the reason for the development of intense business competition after 1887?

Describe the Taylor System.

Who were the four pioneers in the development of industrial management?

CHAPTER III

Expansion of Industrial Enterprises

1. *Trend toward large manufacturing organizations.*
A manufacturing enterprise which employed 800 to 1,000 workers was considered at one time to be a large establishment. Between 1921 and 1929, however, enterprises were built up to a much larger size. Corporations employing 5,000 workers became common, while those with 10,000 workers were not considered unusual. In fact, some companies were developed to a point where they employed as many as 40,000 to 50,000 people. Today, at the middle of the century, there are many companies which are even larger.

In their growth, many manufacturing concerns reached a point where they found it was not economical to concentrate more than a certain number of employees in one plant. They found, however, that by establishing additional plants and dividing their employees among them, they could continue to expand. For example, General Motors now works upon the definite policy of decentralized operation, and has a number of individual manufacturing plants with coordinated control.

It is this movement towards decentralization which has enabled corporations to reach their present great size. Decentralization has made possible their continued expansion, regardless of the fact that the size of any given factory is limited by the dictates of the law of diminishing returns. As will be brought out later, consolidation, integration, and the use of the holding company have played an important part in this movement.

2. *Some measures of size.* It is common and convenient to speak of the size of industrial establishments in terms of the number of wage earners employed. This method is valuable and significant when used to compare establishments similar in nature, but is likely to be extremely misleading when dissimilar plants are studied. For example, a plant producing essentially a handmade product will require more workers than a plant which has a much larger output and specializes in machine-made products.

The amount of invested capital is a second method for measuring the size of plants. It permits the comparison of unlike establishments, but may be unreliable because of the difficulty of obtaining accurate financial information. The value of product, or the value added by manufacture, provides another means of measuring the size of industrial establishments. Carefully compiled statistics pertaining to these matters are made available by the United States Department of Commerce, Census of Manufactures. The various means of measuring size can also be used to measure the expansion of enterprises.

Expansion of Industrial Enterprises

3. *The nature of expansion.* In general, industrial and business organizations tend to expand in one of four ways—sometimes in two or more of these ways at once. The first way is by natural growth, with the establishment expanding by enlargement of the original unit. This added or accretionary growth is frequently referred to as *aggregation.*

The second method of expansion is *horizontal* in character. Such growth takes place when industries of a similar nature combine under one management by merger or amalgamation. In combinations of this kind, there is usually no marked change in materials, processes, or product. Often the reason for such a combination is to enjoy the advantages of centralized purchasing, advertising, and technical facilities.

The third manner of expansion is *vertical* in character. Here, control of materials and processes is extended downward toward the source of raw materials, or upward to control effectively the marketing of the finished product, or in both directions, with the finished product of one establishment becoming the raw material of the next.

The fourth form of expansion is the complementary or *circular* form. This occurs when there is expansion into fields entirely foreign to the parent company except for some remote relationship.

There are other forms of combinations which may be viewed as variations of those discussed above. One of the most important of these is the chain formed by a combination of retail business units. Outstanding examples of chain stores are the food chains, drug chains and auto supply chains.

4. *Trends in mergers.* Mergers are most prevalent when business is good and expansion holds promise of greatest success. The urge to expand is most tempting after a period of wide changes in production and distribution techniques. Such a period followed World War II, and the trend toward the widening of the manufacturing and sales activities of existing organizations is likely to continue for a considerable period.

Since World War II, there have been readjustments rather than attempts at monopoly which to some extent characterized previous expansion periods, and now are subject to being broken up by government action under the anti-trust laws. Companies are now seeking to gain advantages from diversified output, the manufacture of new products and entry into new markets.

Acquisition of going concerns is often the quickest, easiest and cheapest way to enlarge an enterprise. It has the advantage of an established production history, existing markets and customer good will. Furthermore, it brings along the "know how" of those who have been engaged in the business.

5. *Reason for expansion in size.* A primary reason why a company endeavors to expand in size is the fact that large-scale production, within certain economic limits, has various advantages. As a rule, unit manufacturing costs decrease as the number of units manufactured in-

Expansion of Industrial Enterprises

creases. Concomitant with this economic advantage come the benefits of congregated labor, increased purchasing power, and the possibility of lower fixed charges per unit of product produced.

Moreover, a large organization, through the wide scope of its dealings and its national advertising, is in a strong position to build up good will and prestige, which, together with the stability and permanence that a large organization signifies, exert a powerful influence in marketing channels. Thus, for example, a purchaser is more likely to buy a General Electric motor than a similar product manufactured by a smaller company.

A further marked advantage which a large organization has is its ability to employ a high grade of personnel in research, design, and marketing, as well as in the higher administrative brackets. It is interesting to note that one of the reasons for the formation of the large electrical companies was to bring into one organization the large number of small independent research workers in that field. A small organization could not adequately compensate these highly trained technicians, nor could it supply proper facilities and equipment to further the research that was so sorely needed. Today, the General Electric Company, Westinghouse Electric Corporation, and American Telephone and Telegraph Company have large well-established and highly-organized divisions for research and creative endeavors.

Other important forces which accentuate the trend

toward larger enterprises are the abundance of the natural resources of the United States and Canada, the tariffs, the influence of patent and copyright laws, the desire for high profits, and the urge on the part of some to avoid or employ unfair methods of competition.

6. *Expansion by aggregation or accretion.* Expansion by aggregation or accretion takes place in two principal ways. First, an enterprise may expand because of an increase in the number of varieties and sizes of the products which it is called upon to produce. Advances in engineering and other sciences, as well as the growth of population, have been largely responsible for this kind of expansion. Examples are provided by the plants constructing the modern large steamships, locomotives and bridges, and by the gas and electric light and power plants, and water works.

Second, an industry may expand by increasing the number of its tools or processes. In the automobile and textile industries, in the manufacture of typewriters, guns and telephones, and in certain highly specialized or single purpose plants, this manner of accretion is particularly noteworthy. Such plants, if they are to retain their original characteristics, grow by paralleling existing machines and processes with machines and processes of a similar nature.

7. *Horizontal combinations.* As has been stated, industries of a similar nature may expand by using the horizontal method of expansion, that is, by combining under one management. Enterprises of this sort are

Expansion of Industrial Enterprises

termed consolidations. They may take the form of outright amalgamations in which all of the units in the new combination drop their old names and use the name of the consolidation, or they may be in the form of mergers, in which some one company absorbs one or more others and assumes the name for the new combination.

Dwight Farnham, speaking of the combination movement before the American Management Association, listed a number of clear-cut advantages for this type of expansion. He said, in part, that consolidation:

(a) Tends to insure a lower cost of production through continuous quantity production of standardized articles.

(b) Saves expense through the consolidation of administrative, executive, sales, advertising, and similar departments and activities.

(c) Saves transportation charges on raw material and finished products.

(d) Provides for pooling of knowledge, methods, and processes.

(e) Makes possible mass purchases—with added assurance of uniform quality and low cost of raw materials.

(f) Makes maintenance of superior quality possible.

(g) Reduces interest and depreciation on stores of raw material, semi-finished and finished products.

(h) Reduces amount of capital required per unit produced.

(i) Increases ease of financing, since securities are more liquid and more stable.

(j) Permits the most effective use of research facilities.

(k) Increases the security of patents and trademarks.

(l) Permits the use of a high grade of administrators and executives.

(m) Permits retention of highest class of staff experts, lawyers, engineers, chemists, accountants, statisticians, etc.

(n) Makes comparative management possible together with the most effective administrative methods.

8. *Vertical combination or integration.* Integration, as has been previously pointed out, is expansion in a vertical manner. This method consists of taking measures to control all, or some major fraction, of the stages in the development of raw materials into the finished product, including the agencies by which the product is distributed to the consumer. In highly integrated industries, the finished product of one establishment becomes the raw material of the succeeding establishment.

This movement probably originated in the mind of Andrew Carnegie, who believed in "paying a profit to nobody." He put his ideas into practice when he formed the Carnegie Steel Company, and blazed the way for similar integrations in the steel business, as

Expansion of Industrial Enterprises

well as in other lines. The Stinnes Konzern in Germany, until its collapse in 1925, was the most powerful and widely publicized integrated combination anywhere in the world.

There are, however, many modern noteworthy examples of integration. The Anaconda Copper Mining Company, the various Standard Oil Companies, the meat packers of Chicago—all have learned the lessons of "verticalization." There are also companies in which the process has not been extended so completely through the organization structure. Examples of these partially integrated enterprises are the American Telephone and Telegraph Company, with its subsidiaries; Sears, Roebuck & Company, with its manufacturing plants; and many concerns producing textiles, food, and baking products.

Economically, vertical growth is justified on very much the same grounds as consolidation. Even though transportation costs may be slightly higher, and although comparative management may not be important, since the quality of raw materials and the stabilization of their costs are assured, the integrated management occupies a very strong competitive position. Furthermore, payment for raw materials and semiprocessed materials in the form of book credits between succeeding integrated units, eliminates the necessity of carrying the usual amount of cash reserves. In cases of destructive competition, such integrated enterprises, particularly when coupled by consolidation, become exceedingly powerful and are likely to incur severe legal restrictions.

To be successful, an integrated enterprise should consist of a balanced structure; each unit should be able to employ the complete output of the unit which precedes it, and each unit should produce materials efficiently and at low cost. If this should not be true, certain establishments of the integrated chain would be compelled to "purchase" materials at higher prices than those quoted in the open market. One of the greatest difficulties with the vertical integration is that of keeping abreast of technical developments of various processes so as to keep the cost of operation below the open market price.

9. *The circular industry.* The circular or allied combination unites industries manufacturing products alike or complementary in nature, or products that can be readily sold in the same market. Quite similar to consolidation, this form of combination furnishes many interesting examples. One of the oldest and most successful is the International Business Machines Corporation which manufactures computing, tabulating, and recording devices. Remington Rand, Incorporated, furnishes another outstanding example through its ability to supply a complete line of equipment for modern business use.

Allied combinations derive much competitive power from their ability to allocate a single product to certain highly specialized plants within their group.

Expansion of Industrial Enterprises

This makes it possible for them to obtain important results in costs and efficiencies.

10. *Chain combinations.* Chains of many types exist. Included among them are chains of stores, banks, hotels, bakeries and theaters. Yearly sales through these channels run up into billions of dollars. Dwight Farnham, in "Economic Types of Combinations," summarizes the reasons for the chain-store movement as follows:

(a) Increased efficiency secured by means of standardization, mass production, labor-saving machinery and more exact methods of management.

(b) Increase in the cost of distribution from high pressure sales methods, large advertising appropriations, and the coverage of greater territories for the purpose of disposing of greater volume.

(c) Disappearance of retail outlets in small towns because of the popularity of the automobile and the construction of highways.

(d) General weakness and inefficiency of the small retailer as a class.

The development of standardized methods of retailing, based on the scientific determination of such controlling factors as store location, layout, high turnover goods, and the buying habits of the public, assisted the growth of the chain store to the point where mass buying direct from the manufacturer became possible. In some cases, vertical integration extends from the purchase of raw material to the disposal of goods to the ultimate consumer, as in the case of manufacturers and mail-order chains.

11. *The holding-company method of combination.* The holding company offers a method of consolidation through stockholders. One or more companies may unite their interests by delegating the controlling interest of each to a new organization, and thus create what is known as a holding company.

Under this plan, the holding or parent company, in buying the controlling interest in a company, generally a majority of its stock, pays for it by issues of its own stock, or by cash from the sale of its own securities. Control in hand, the holding company then elects its own majority directors to the boards of its various subsidiaries, and proceeds to direct their activities to suit its aims. Thus, each company may retain its identity, and yet avoid the hazards of competition and realize the full benefits of consolidation.

Public utilities have been particularly active in this field, the American Telephone and Telegraph Company having followed this principle for some time. Federal legislation now limits holding companies to those of the second degree, that is, one holding company can own the stock of another, but the second can own only stocks of actual manufacturing or operating companies. This regulation was set up to prevent pyramiding and the formation of monopolies.

Expansion of Industrial Enterprises

12. *Importance of the smaller plant in the industrial structure.* While we may expect to see the continual development of large organizations, especially in those fields of manufacturing in which products tend to become staple and standardized, the prospect is that small industries will continue to play an important part in the nation's economy. Census data show that about 92 per cent of the manufacturing establishments are in the group employing less than 500 persons each. Increased sales effort, better advertising, market research, product development, reduction in operating expenses, installation of modern equipment, and other progressive measures are the factors which make possible the success of these small companies.

Review

Why is decentralization necessary to continued expansion of an enterprise?

What are some of the measured rods which are used for the purpose of determining the size and growth of an industrial establishment?

Explain briefly the following four ways in which an enterprise may expand: accretion, horizontal, vertical, circular.

What is a company's primary reason for endeavoring to expand? Give some other reasons.

In what two principal ways may an enterprise expand by accretion?

What are some of the advantages of expanding by the horizontal method?

In expanding by the vertical method, what are some of the prerequisites to success?

Give an example of an enterprise which has successfully expanded by the circular method.

Give some reasons for the growth of chain-stores.

Describe the holding-company method of combination.

CHAPTER IV

Plant Location

1. *Factors in plant location.* There are seven primary factors which industries generally take into consideration in determining where they will locate their plants. As listed by the United States Census, these factors are as follows:

- (a) Nearness to raw materials.
- (b) Nearness to markets.
- (c) Availability of water power.
- (d) Favorable climate.
- (e) A supply of labor.
- (f) Capital available for investment.
- (g) The momentum of an early start.

2. *Raw materials and markets.* An industry is established either because there is a demand for a product, or because it is expected that such a demand can be created. In the main, an enterprise tends to locate near that center which it expects to serve. Nevertheless, the availability of raw materials is also an important economic factor, and this may force a location compromise because of transportation rates and facilities.

It is poor economy to ship bulky or perishable raw materials long distances if a large portion of such materials becomes waste in the process of manufacture. Consequently, industries of this type tend to locate near the sources of their supplies. For example, many of the large pulp and paper mills are found near forests; the salmon-canning industries have settled along the Columbia River; the oyster industries at Baltimore; and the meat-packing industries at Chicago.

Sources of raw materials and markets become of less importance in the matter of plant location as transportation becomes cheaper. If transportation costs are small, then labor or power, or a combination of the two, may be the controlling influence in locating an industry. With low transportation costs, both raw materials and finished products may be efficiently transported long distances and still find a profitable market, if an industry is located where labor and power conditions are favorable.

3. *Water power.* Water power was of tremendous importance during the days before steam power, when many industries obtained their start. The abundant waterfalls of New England contributed immeasurably to her industrial prominence. The wool and cotton mills which spread throughout her territory, and the great writing-paper industrial center at Holyoke are indicators of the importance of water power in early manufacturing. With the coming into use of coal and oil for supplying power, New England lost her preeminence. Industry found that other sections of the country had equal, if not superior, manufacturing advantages.

Plant Location

Later, water power again became important since it provided a means of generating electricity. Great industries grew about centers where hydroelectric power was plentiful. The grouping of industries in the vicinity of Niagara Falls is a good example. The industries of the Pacific Coast, particularly those near Los Angeles, also grew and multiplied rapidly because of an abundance of water power, popularly known as "white coal," which makes electric power relatively low in price.

The trend of power development in sections where water power is available at low enough cost is toward huge, efficient, central stations operated by water power. Where water power is not available, the trend is in the direction of steam turbines, a field in which the technology of coal combustion is constantly decreasing the quantity of coal consumed per kilowatt hour. Use is also being made of diesels and gas turbines in the production of electricity.

Electricity produced by privately-owned factory, municipal, and farm power plants will be eventually replaced by cheaper current purchased from central stations. Wireless transmission of power is also a possibility in the not too distant future, and the applications of atomic energy yet remain to be explored.

4. *Climate.* A healthful, vigorous climate is conducive to increased industrial production, and usually the most satisfactory site for a manufacturing establishment is in an area which has a certain variation in climatic conditions, but does not suffer from extremes of

heat and cold. Nevertheless, a mild climate may have certain advantages. For example, shipbuilders can work in the open in San Francisco in comparative comfort all the year around, while such work in the northeastern section of the United States is a matter of great hardship and expense.

Today, however, climate is a less important factor than formerly. In the past, many companies were compelled, because of some requirement of their manufacturing process, to take into consideration the presence, or absence, of humidity, sunshine, or some other climatic variation in deciding on the location of their plants. At the present time, improvement in air conditioning apparatus and technique makes it possible for many factories to operate satisfactorily in almost any type of climate.

5. *Labor supply.* In industries where a large part of the labor is of the semi-skilled and unskilled variety, the matter of securing an adequate labor supply carries less weight than other factors in choosing a site for a factory. Workers can either be found in the locality of a chosen site, or they can be moved from another locality where employment opportunities are scarce.

In the case of industries requiring skilled workers, however, factories usually have to be located where such workers are available. Skilled labor cannot be found in any locality, and it is difficult to move it from other places without a considerable increase in wages or other forms of compensation. In the first place,

Plant Location

workers do not like to leave the homes to which they are accustomed. In the second place, when workers are skilled, there is usually little economic pressure to make them go elsewhere to earn a living, since the local demand for their services is so great that they can easily obtain jobs in the place where they live.

If, therefore, highly skilled labor is necessary for the success of an industry, the management can do little else than to establish its plant in a community which can provide this type of labor. This is the prime requirement and it must be met even though, from the point of view of raw materials or markets, the location may not be the most desirable.

6. *Capital.* Whether or not an area provides a potential source of capital may be a factor to take into consideration in choosing a site for an industry. While large enterprises are usually financed at the large money centers, small and medium-size industries are frequently "floated" by means of local capital. In the case of large enterprises not dependent on local capital, factories may be built in almost any location which has other favorable features.

In the case of smaller industries, however, the choice of location is usually limited by the fact that they are dependent on capitalists outside of the large money centers, and these capitalists generally insist that their investments be kept in their immediate vicinity. Consequently, a small enterprise often finds that a desirable place to locate is a prosperous town or city, where money is being made rapidly in old established industries and loaned to new industries.

7. *The effect of modern influences.* The 1929–1932 depression, the subsequent recovery, and finally World War II, which brought with it the greatest industrial activity of all time, greatly affected the location of industry in the United States and Canada. This course of events accelerated to a marked degree long-term trends involving, (1) a migration of plants and of whole industries to new locations, (2) a process of decentralization in manufacturing, (3) a rise of new competition in new places.

These trends may be partly accounted for by the influence of the motor car, new road materials, huge power transmission systems, diesel engine power, and faster means of communication and transportation. Government legislation has also been a factor in the situation. Management has had to adapt itself to new laws in connection with production and labor. Marketing in all its phases has had to be revised to meet new conditions. Finance has been greatly affected by the Securities Exchange Act.

8. *Plant relocations.* A check survey made in the recent past indicated that plant location was a matter of major concern to a large percentage of industrial companies. About half of the companies indicated that they were considering extensive changes in the physical facilities of their factories, such as new layouts, new equipment, factory reconstruction and new buildings,

Plant Location

and of these companies, half were weighing the question of moving to new locations. It is likely that industries will introduce a far higher degree of flexibility in physical plant factors in the future, and that moving of plants, or expansion by decentralization, will be practiced to a considerably greater degree than in the past.

One factor in determining some of the relocations in the future will be the defense angle. This will result in the scattering of plants from munitions manufacturing centers into separate and widely distributed areas to avoid the large losses of production which would be incurred by air-bombing damage in concentrated regions. Certain plant construction will be in bomb-proof underground locations to protect workers and machinery in case of aerial attack. One such plant is that of Smith & Wesson, at Springfield, Massachusetts.

9. *Underlying reasons for plant migration.* There are, however, various underlying reasons for plant migration, and these differ widely among industries. One of the principal reasons why an industry decides to move is the fact that in the assembly of raw materials some other location will enable it to reduce its transportation and handling costs sufficiently to justify the move.

Among other reasons for moving are better labor markets, fewer obstructive state laws, lower taxes, and more considerate local governments in other sections of the country. Instances can be cited where large concerns moved only a few miles across the border to an adjoining state. By doing so, they were able to obtain great reductions in taxes and more friendly working relations and, at the same time, hold a large majority of their trained working force.

10. *Decentralization.* A special aspect of this migration of industries is decentralization. This is not a shifting of plants or whole industries to new locations, but rather the adding of plants in new locations to their existing set-ups in a "spreading out" or decentralizing process.

One of the more familiar types of decentralization is that of the cement industry. A few decades ago, practically all cement produced in the United States was made in the Lehigh Valley of Pennsylvania. Since that time, a combination of high freight rates and low selling prices made it necessary for producers to establish additional plants in important marketing areas. Today, every important cement company that operates on a national basis has numerous plants. Those of the Lehigh Portland Cement Company are scattered across the country in ten states; the International Cement Corporation has plants in eight states; Alpha Portland Cement Company operates in seven states.

In the canning industry, large interests were forced into decentralization from the start, since canning could not be successfully done unless the plants were located at or near the points where crops were grown. For instance, California Packing Corporation, largest single factor in its field, has 75 separate canning plants in the state of California. Furthermore, the companies man-

Plant Location

ufacturing the cans soon found that it was much more to their advantage to ship sheet tin plate than finished cans into the canning centers. American Can Company now operates over 50 plants, while Continental Can Company has nearly that number of separate units.

The Ford Motor Company, long a proponent of decentralization and the small plant in the country, has a considerable number of small plants located at strategic points. Each one of these plants is on a river where water power runs the machines at a saving in power cost. Many advantages result from such decentralization. These may be summed up as follows:

Advantages of Decentralization to the Employer:
- (a) Better quality of work.
- (b) Low time and money cost and low overhead charges.
- (c) Development of pride and skill.
- (d) Greater interest in work.
- (e) Less lost time.
- (f) Small labor turnover.
- (g) Facility in changing and improving methods.
- (h) Close relationship between men and management.

Advantages of Decentralization to the Employee:
- (a) Probability of steady work.
- (b) Opportunity to develop individual aptitudes.
- (c) Living amid village or country surroundings.
- (d) Opportunity to cultivate a plot of land.
- (e) A more comfortable tempo of life.
- (f) A high level of neighborhood character.

11. *Labor unrest.* A factor of importance to consider in choosing the location for a plant is the extent to which the area suffers from labor unrest. In certain areas, unions have extended their memberships and influence, and have undertaken pressure campaigns to bring workers in nearby unorganized plants into the unions. Workers who may have no desire for unionization are often subjected to this pressure, and hence work under a strain.

Furthermore, discontent among some workers in such areas is likely to lead automatically to uncertainty and restlessness among all workers. A strike in one place frequently spreads to other plants, or at least raises issues in such plants. Certain cities are nationally well-known for chronic labor discontent, frequent slowdowns of work, and other concerted disturbances arising among labor groups. This unrest exhibits itself even in plants where wages, working conditions and other industrial-relations factors are quite satisfactory to employees.

As a result, many companies which are not often plagued by labor troubles from internal causes decide to relocate in other areas where their employees will not be disturbed by labor unrest prevailing outside of their plants. Furthermore, by making such a move, they can add to the contentment of their workers by giving them better living conditions, superior working facilities, a better-laid-out and more efficient plant with all modern conveniences, and a community life far superior to the social isolation typical of most of the larger cities and manufacturing centers. The prevalence of general labor unrest has thus contributed to the migration of industries to other localities.

12. *The product and the plant site.* Before a decision can be reached upon the kind of plant site desirable in a particular instance, careful consideration must be given to the products to be manufactured. Hence, engineers should be called upon to make exhaustive studies as to the nature or designs of the products, as well as to their value and the volumes in which they will be produced. Will the process be continuous, repetitive, or intermittent? What type of machinery and equipment will be required? What services in the way of water, gas, compressed air, and electricity will be necessary? These and many similar questions must be answered in order to assure that the plant site selected will prove suitable for the manufacturer's purpose.

13. *Locating the plant.* The problem of choosing a suitable plant site resolves itself into three major subdivisions: (1) choosing the general territory within a selected region; (2) selecting the particular community; (3) deciding upon the specific factory site in that community.

14. *Choosing the general territory.* A number of important factors must be considered in choosing the general territory within the region selected as the most desirable for the location of a projected plant. W. G. Holmes in *Plant Location,* lists these factors as follows:

(a) Market.
(b) Raw materials.
(c) Transportation facilities.
(d) Freight rates.
(e) Labor and wages.
(f) Fuel and power.
(g) Laws and taxation.
(h) Favorable climate.
(i) Water supply.
(j) Building costs.
(k) Cost of living.
(l) Population.
(m) Attitude of legislators toward industries.
(n) Capital from local sources.

The foregoing study, as well as other studies which have been made of factors to consider in selecting a plant site, leads to the inevitable conclusion that the most advantageous plant location is that location in which the sum of manufacturing and marketing costs is at a minimum.

15. *Community selection.* The selection of the particular local community in which a plant shall be located involves a consideration of some other factors besides those previously enumerated. Some of the more important of these factors are as follows:

(a) Size of the community.
(b) Transportation facilities, external and internal.
(c) Initial building requirements and possibility of expansion.

Plant Location

(d) Availability of electric power.
(e) Supply of specialized labor.
(f) Dependence upon other industries.
(g) Financial considerations and financial institutions.
(h) Relative effort of community restrictions and community aid.
(i) Relative value of local markets.
(j) Good living conditions.

16. *Size of community.* Of fundamental importance in the foregoing list of factors bearing upon the selection of a particular community is the question of its size. It must be decided as to which of the following offer the most advantageous location: (a) large cities; (b) small cities and towns; (c) suburban locations; (d) rural locations. This range of choice may be increased by consideration of various city sections, industrial towns which adjoin cities, and privately organized and controlled industrial districts.

17. *Selecting the factory site.* When the particular community has been chosen, there still remains the problem of definitely selecting the factory site in the community. This is a problem which requires the most careful thought and planning. Factors to be considered in making a choice are as follows:

(a) Land values.
(b) Character of site.
  (1) Contour of the ground.
  (2) Soil conditions.

64 *Plant Management*

      (3) Shape of tract or plot.
- (c) Room for expansion.
- (d) Housing facilities.
- (e) Public improvements.
    - (1) Sewers.
    - (2) Pavements.
    - (3) Police and fire protection.
- (f) Utility services.
    - (1) Power and light.
    - (2) Gas.
    - (3) Water supply.
    - (4) Transportation of labor.
- (g) Approach and trackage for freight.
- (h) Approach and wharf for waterway delivery and shipments.
- (i) Labor.
    - (1) Kind.
    - (2) Quantity.
- (j) Environment.
    - (1) Smoke.
    - (2) Dust.
    - (3) Odors.
    - (4) Noise.
- (k) Disposal of waste.
- (l) Building laws.
- (m) Local ordinances.
- (n) Taxes.
- (o) Future of site.
- (p) Express and postal service.
- (q) General limitations of site.
- (r) Financial aids.

Plant Location

18. *Method of selecting a plant site.* In selecting a specific plant site, there are several methods of analysis which can be used. When there are two or three different sites from which to make a choice, a method of considerable merit is to weight the various factors along the lines illustrated by Figure 2. The first column in this illustration gives the weight which it is figured each of six factors should have if the location were ideal for the industry under consideration. The value of each of these factors for each of the three locations shown in the next three columns is then determined by comparing the actual locations with the ideal location. The location which has the six factors adding up to the highest total is the one to be selected. In the case of the illustration, Location A is the choice with 79 points out of a possible 100, as compared with 73 for Location B and 54 for Location C.

19. *Cost comparisons as a method of plant location.* The problem of selecting a plant location by means of cost comparisons may be divided into three parts: (1) cost of raw materials, (2) cost of manufacture, and (3) cost of distribution. Costs may be computed for a unit of production, as a barrel of cement, or for a given total quantity, or for a volume of output in a unit of time, as for a week, month, or year. After these costs are arrived at for each location under consideration, they will provide a basis for comparing the several locations and determining the relative advantage of each. The location selected will be the one where the esti-

Plant Requirements	Value Ideal Location	Location A	Location B	Location C
Markets	35	35	25	20
Transportation	25	15	15	10
Raw materials	15	10	15	15
Labor	10	5	10	5
Power	10	10	5	2
Climate	5	4	3	2
Totals	100	79	73	54

Figure 2—Use of Weighted Factors in Selecting a Plant Site

Plant Location

mates show the plant will benefit from the lowest costs.

The cost of raw material in each case will include purchase price at source, plus transportation costs. Manufacturing costs will include all operating costs, plus a consideration of cost of such items as buildings, land, and taxes. Distribution costs may be more difficult to estimate, but with past experience as a guide and a knowledge of market areas, they can be determined with reasonable accuracy.

An illustration of the manner in which these costs are tabulated for comparison of one location with others is given by W. Gerald Holmes, in *Plant Location*, and is shown in Figure 3.

COST FACTOR		Site A	Site B	Site C	Site D
Raw materials at the mill	Limestone	$0.14	$0.16	$0.13	$0.10
	Shale	0.02	0.03	0.02	0.03
	Gypsum	0.04	0.04	0.04	0.04
Fuel and power	Coal	0.27	0.19	0.30	0.22
	Electrical energy	0.18	0.22	0.26	0.20
Works expense	Mill labor, superintendence	0.14	0.16	0.12	0.14
	Laboratory, repair parts, etc.	0.08	0.08	0.09	0.08
General expense and charges	Administration and incidentals	0.06	0.05	0.05	0.05
	Insurance	0.01	0.01	0.01	0.01
	Taxes (including income)	0.06	0.08	0.10	0.08
	Bond interest	0.05	0.05	0.05	0.05
	Amortization	0.06	0.06	0.06	0.06
	Packing, sack cleaning and sack loss	0.07	0.07	0.07	0.07
	Sales	0.10	0.09	0.10	0.11
	Transportation (to market.)	0.33	0.24	0.30	0.40
Totals		$1.61	$1.53	$1.70	$1.64

FIGURE 3—COMPUTATIONS OF DELIVERED-TO-CUSTOMERS COST IN SELECTING THE LOCATION OF CEMENT MILL. COSTS ARE PER BARREL.

Plant Management

By delivered-to-customers cost is meant the total of all costs which a commodity must bear from the time the raw material is taken from nature until the finished goods are delivered to the manufacturer's customers. It includes not only all manufacturing costs, but also the price which must be paid for raw materials, transportation charges to the factory, and transportation charges on the finished goods from factory to customer.

The tabulation in Figure 3 shows the computation of delivered-to-customers cost for four possible locations of a cement mill which is to supply a certain metropolitan market, in which it is believed the mill's output of 1,000,000 barrels of cement will be sold.

Examination of the tabulation shows that the lowest cost is for Location B with a delivered-to-customers cost of $1.53 per barrel. The principal advantages of the location are the low fuel and power cost, and the low distribution expense. These provide an offset to the fact that the raw materials cost and mill labor cost are higher than for any of the other locations. This brings out the importance of taking into account not only operating costs but also distribution costs in selecting the location for a plant. In other words, the cost of all factors involved in carrying on a business should be considered in choosing a site.

20. *Emergency locations.* War or other emergencies frequently throw an emphasis upon the speed with which a plant can be built and products produced. In the selection of the Detroit area for the tank factory

Plant Location

to be built and operated by the Chrysler Corporation for the War Department during World War II, the promise of greater speed in delivery outweighed every other consideration.

Emergency may affect the selection of locations in other ways, however. For example, World War II caused the War Department to decide to place its plants in the interior of the country in order to minimize the hazard of attack from the air.

Emergencies, however, do not mean that consideration is not also given to the economic factors which private industry would normally take into account in selecting a plant location. In picking a site for a defense plant, the War Department considers the availability of power to meet not only the first but also the expanded needs of such a plant. It also takes into account the transportation factor as a means not only of carrying the raw materials to the factory, but also of taking it away in its finished form. River, canal and road facilities, as well as those of the plane and the freight car, are all given due consideration.

Review

What seven primary factors, according to the United States Census, does an industry consider in selecting a location for its plant?

What three long-term trends in the location of industry were accelerated by the course of events after 1929?

Give some of the underlying reasons for plant migration.

Name some of the advantages of decentralization.

Explain why it is often beneficial for a company with good internal labor relations to move from a city where general labor unrest is a chronic condition.

In locating a plant, what factors should be taken into consideration in selecting the general territory? In selecting the community in that territory? In selecting the exact site in the chosen community?

Describe a method of selecting a plant site through the use of weighted factors.

How may cost comparisons be used in locating a plant?

How may emergencies affect the locations of plants?

CHAPTER V

Principles of Mass Production

1. *Modern manufacturing principles.* Successful modern manufacturing is based upon certain well-established principles, among the most important of which are specialization, division of labor, transfer of skill, standardization, interchangeability of parts, and simplification. Specialization and division of labor are nearly as old as the human race. Standardization, interchangeability, and simplification entered into the picture later with the development of modern methods of industrial organization and operation.

2. *Specialization.* Specialization is the concentration of effort upon a limited field of endeavor. At an early date, men found that by confining their labors to certain definite activities they could produce goods of better quality at lower cost. Specialization is often used synonymously with division of labor, but it is also used in a broader sense to cover the specialization of industries, individual manufacturing establishments, occupations or callings, and even geographical divisions.

Division of labor, on the other hand, is most generally used to apply to the activities of an individual worker. Division of labor is well illustrated in modern manufacturing, where the work of producing an article is divided among a number of workers, each person performing a very limited part of the total task.

3. *Specialization in manufacturing.* It was a common occurrence some years ago to find single establishments —large machine or jobbing shops—producing many different lines of products. As industry developed, however, and as competition became keener, manufacturers found that by limiting their field to fewer lines, and obtaining larger volume in these lines, they not only could reduce their costs but also manufacture articles of a higher grade.

Science and invention greatly accelerated this process of specialization. With the widespread adoption of scientific methods, manufacturers found that it was difficult enough to keep up-to-date on one or two lines, to say nothing of half a dozen. Furthermore, many industries dependent upon certain patents or chemical processes came into being, and many so-called "continuous process" industries, such as salt, paint, and cement plants, were established. The very nature of the processes of these industries dictated that they operate in a very specialized field.

4. *Geographical specialization.* The process of specialization in manufacturing has led to a certain amount of geographical specialization. Thus, New York City is a local point for the production of clothing, Pittsburgh for steel, Detroit for automobiles, Chicago for meat, and Akron for rubber. Conceivably, one locality may

Principles of Mass Production

occupy itself chiefly with the manufacture of some single part of a final product. In the automotive industry, for example, the final assembly plant may receive engines from one town, axles from another, and wheels, springs, and frames from still other localities.

5. *Specialization in marketing.* The marketing activities carried on by middlemen furnish a good example of specialization in the field of distribution, and there is a real economic justification for their existence. In general, the cost to most manufacturers of supplying each consumer direct with the quantities he desires is prohibitive. Specialty stores, or strictly one-line stores, handling such goods as hats, hosiery, candy, or orange juice, are growing rapidly in number, and are excellent examples of the principle of marketing specialization.

6. *Specialization of callings.* Because of the introduction of modern machine processes, many of the older trades or callings have been greatly modified, and some have even disappeared. The handicraft shoemaker, the blacksmith, and, to a certain extent, the cabinetmaker, no longer play a prominent part in economic society. New industries, however, are constantly giving rise to new occupations; sometimes they adopt an old trade, as the automobile industry did for the carriage maker; in other cases, they create entirely new callings. Electric welding is markedly different from the ways of the old-fashioned blacksmith; the manufacture of rayon and the modern plastic fibers is quite unlike the culture of the silkworm.

7. *Advantages of specialization.* Through specialization, several obvious advantages accrue. Goods of higher quality can be produced, and, what is equally significant, they can be manufactured more cheaply. Humanity is undoubtedly thus benefited. Furthermore, a means of livelihood is extended to countless thousands of persons who are able to perform simple specialized operations and obtain higher wages than they could obtain in other lines of endeavor.

The extent to which specialization can be carried, however, depends on the quantity that can be produced, and this quantity is controlled by the available market. Consequently, before expenditures for highly specialized tools and apparatus for the manufacture of specialized articles are made, they should be scrutinized with extreme care, and should be based on a careful analysis of the market for the products to be manufactured.

8. *Division of labor.* While the terms "specialization" and "division of labor" are frequently used synonymously, the latter is the term more generally used to apply to the refined specialization of the individual worker. In the modern factory, there are many individual and distinct operations. The process of manufacturing a product is reduced to a point where only one or a few of these operations are performed by each "operation specialist" who may not even be aware of the ultimate value of his endeavors.

The most extensive application of this procedure is

Principles of Mass Production

found in the larger industries, particularly where repetitive methods of a semiautomatic nature are possible. The general tendency is to subdivide all kinds of work into simple detailed operations that can be performed by operators who are generally incapable of performing the complete list of operations required for the finished part. The assembly line of a modern automobile plant furnishes an interesting example, and is described by Dexter S. Kimball, former dean of the College of Engineering, Cornell University, in the following manner:

> An assembly line consists essentially of a benchlike framework 500 or 600 feet long fitted with guiding surfaces along which the automobile progresses during assembly. At the starting end, the frame of the automobile is placed upon the guides and fastened by a carrier to an endless chain that moves along between the guiding surfaces at the rate of 2 or 3 feet per minute. The several parts of the automobile are supplied by carriers to fixed points on the assembly line in the order in which they are to be assembled.
>
> At each station are groups of workers whose sole duty it is to assemble the part that is supplied to them in the time allowed by the speed of the chain. Thus, a man may do nothing but insert a given bolt, and screw it into place. He may be provided with a wrench that automatically regulates the degree of tightness with which the bolt is set up, thus further reducing the mental and physical requirements of

the operation so that almost anyone can be taught in a short time to do the work.

It should be noted, also, that the time element is controlled by the chain so that if a man is compelled for any reason whatever to drop out, another must take his place no matter how small or detailed the operation may be; otherwise the entire assembly is held up. By the time the machine reaches the end of the line, it is completely assembled, and leaves the line under its own power.

Similar methods are employed in assembling automobile engines, which are placed in the automobile during its assembly as a self-contained unit. The rate at which both engine and car can be assembled by these methods is surprisingly great compared to the older methods where the same group of men completed the assembly.

9. *Other forms of division of labor.* It must not be inferred, however, that division of labor takes place only in the field of manual operations. Production labor is mental as well as manual, and there is quite likely to be division of mental labor or division of thought. The mental labor of designing is largely performed apart from the actual productive process and may be divided among the chief designer, his assistants, and a corps of draftsmen and tracers.

In the process of controlling production, there is also a marked subdivision of effort. The planning department does the mental work of routing and scheduling the products through the factory, with the produc-

Principles of Mass Production

tion manager and his assistants dividing this mental task among them.

10. *Transfer of skill.* Transfer of skill is the basic idea underlying tool construction. While it is not directly related to division of labor, it does permit the extension of this important principle. What is meant by transfer of skill may be seen from the following illustration.

Let it be assumed that it is desired to drill four holes in a number of flat plates, each of which is one foot square and one-half inch thick. The holes are to be accurately spaced with reference to the end surfaces of the plates. It is quite obvious that to perform such an operation accurately (say within 0.002 inch) on one plate with an ordinary drill press would require a relatively high degree of skill on the part of the worker. To drill several hundred plates would require not only great skill but the expenditure of a great deal of time. Consequently, the cost of performing such a task might reach an almost prohibitive figure.

To overcome these difficulties, a skilled workman, generally a tool maker, can construct a device known as a "drilling jig." The plate to be drilled can then be placed in this jig where it is securely clamped into position for each drilling operation. The jig contains four holes for the drill to pass through. These holes are located with great care so that they correspond with the required location of the holes in the plates to be drilled. The holes in the jig are surrounded with hardened steel bushings or rings to prevent wear when the drill, which fits the bushings closely and accurately, passes through the holes.

It thus becomes possible for any relatively unskilled person to fit the plates into the jig, operate the drill, and produce a finished plate as accurately as most skilled workmen could without such a device. It would, in fact, be difficult to produce a plate inaccurately if the jig is accurately made, *for the accuracy of the work no longer depends upon the skill of the worker but upon the accuracy of the tool.*

11. *Transfer of thought and intelligence.* It is evident from the illustration of the drilling jig that a large part of the mental labor can be done once and for all by the toolmaker. Through the use of the tool, the unskilled worker needs to expend little or no thought in producing the product. A transfer of thought and intelligence is thus made from person to machine. If the quantity of products to be manufactured is sufficiently large to warrant it, it is possible in many cases to make machines to which all required skill and thought have been transferred. Such machines may not even require an attendant. Machines of this nature are known as full automatics, and thousands are in use in modern industry.

The advancement in electrical engineering gives promise to carry the development of machines to the ultimate of human imagination. For example, the photoelectric cell has revolutionized many of previous methods of doing things. By use of this ingenious de-

Principles of Mass Production

vice, electric light switches can be automatically turned on and off in keeping with the amount of light required, giant steel ingots can be reversed by their own shadows, and white-hot furnaces can be opened by light beams from moving cranes.

12. *Unit cost and its relation to quantity.* Unit cost and its relation to quantity may be illustrated by a simple example. Assume that an individual worker is producing a certain product, the labor cost of one unit of which is $10. Then, in order to simplify the problem further, assume that overhead expense in the form of such items as interest, rent, light and power is so small as to be negligible. In the course of his activities, the worker devises a piece of special apparatus worth $50, which will reduce the labor cost to $2. His problem then is to figure out how much this apparatus will reduce the total cost and how soon will the savings pay for the device. His calculations show that the cost of one unit produced by the new device would be as follows:

$$\frac{\$50 + (\$2 \times 1)}{1} \text{ or } \$52$$

He then finds, by using the same method of calculation, that if he produced two units, the cost of each unit would be

$$\frac{\$50 + (\$2 \times 2)}{2} \text{ or } \$27$$

Three units would cost $18.66 each, four units $14.00, five units $12.00, six units $10.33, and seven units $9.13

each. Thus, he would have to produce at least seven units to recover the cost of his apparatus. For 100 units, the cost would be $2.50 each, for 500 units $2.10 and so on, with the cost decreasing at a slower and slower rate as it approached the theoretical limit of $2.

The foregoing illustration brings out the point once more that quantity is the factor that dictates whether or not it will pay to make special tools for the purpose of transferring skill and extending division of labor. The larger the quantity, the greater may be the expenditures for special tools and preparation costs, but usually the more complete the equipment is, the lower the cost of the product becomes. Low costs stimulate a demand for the product, which, in turn, makes more production possible, and hence, an ever-widening expansion occurs which is limited only by the available market.

13. *Limiting influences.* The relationship between quantity, transfer of skill, and division of labor being thus established, we may state a general principle usually referred to as the law of increasing productivity. The principle is this:

In general, unit cost can be decreased as the quantity to be manufactured is increased.

This principle does not hold indefinitely, however, since apparently every economic gain is accompanied by a corresponding economic loss which tends to offset the effects of that gain. As a result, a certain optimum point will be reached beyond which increases in quantity will not reduce costs and there occurs a stage

Principles of Mass Production

of diminishing returns. This is a well-known principle and it is well established in manufacturing and business operations.

14. *Standardization.* Standardization is the basis of the mass production movement. Without it, modern manufacturing and interchangeability would not be possible. Furthermore, without standards and specifications, marketing would be severely handicapped. Standardization means the reduction of any given line of products to certain fixed types, sizes, and characteristics.

Suppose, for example, a firm decides to specialize in the manufacture of men's shoes. Since no two feet are exactly alike, there is practically no limit to the number of types and sizes that such an organization might produce. Because of practical business considerations, however, production will be confined to a few types and sizes, which, in the opinion of the management, will find a favorable market.

So, instead of measuring each foot and building a shoe especially for it, a limited number of sizes of each type will be manufactured, with the sizes and the numbers in which they are manufactured being determined from previous experience, or from statistics compiled by the shoe trade. The result will be that the *average* man will find in this range of sizes a pair that will fit him, while other buyers will secure a sufficiently close approximation to their exact requirements to satisfy their needs. Such a procedure, which is known as the method of the average solution, is followed in order to make possible quantity production.

15. *Marketing standards.* In marketing, standards indicate quality—quality based upon such factors as size, color, appearance, chemical content, moisture content, strength, and shape. Uniformity may be obtained in this manner, and products may be bought and sold in different localities and at different times upon a set of standard specifications. Wheat, corn, cotton and steel are familiar examples.

Products are graded in accordance with specifications set by certain predetermined standards. For example, the United States Department of Agriculture determines standards for wheat, corn, and cotton, while the United States Bureau of Standards and the various engineering societies set standards for steel, steel products, electrical devices and a wide range of other manufactured products.

16. *Interchangeability.* It is a basic principle in mass production that every machine part or element shall be, within very small limits, exactly like every other similar part. This must necessarily be true, for a factory product is usually the work of many workers, and is assembled on a general assembly floor from parts made by men who may never view the finished product.

In the words of Dean Kimball, "A modern factory is, in fact, like a good sized river, the various elements flowing like branches from different departments and merging smoothly into the stream of the finished prod-

Principles of Mass Production

uct that passes out through the shipping room." Quite obviously, every part must fit and be interchangeable with every like part in order to make possible the use of such methods as these.

17. *Technical aspects of standardization, interchangeability, and inspection.* From a technical and engineering standpoint, modern standardization may be wide or narrow in scope, according to whether the standards are:

(a) International.
(b) National.
(c) Within a particular industry.
(d) Within an individual factory.

18. *International standards.* There are certain basic international standards, such as the ohm, volt, ampere, and meter, which are in constant use as measuring standards. The electrical and chemical industries, in particular, employ such international standard units extensively.

19. *National standards.* The United States Bureau of Standards is largely responsible for the development of basic scientific national standards. One of its typical pieces of work is the development of Hoke standard gages of lengths that are accurate to the millionth part of an inch.

The American Standards Association, Incorporated, (A.S.A.), composed of 67 of the leading technical societies as member-bodies, and over 2,100 sustaining members, including manufacturers, distributors, and associations, was established to further the work of developing national standards and coordinating American developments with those of foreign countries. The A.S.A. is a member of the International Standards Association.

20. *Standards within a particular industry.* The American Society of Mechanical Engineers (A.S.M.E.), the Society of Automotive Engineers (S.A.E.), the Illuminating Engineering Society (I.E.S.), and many other technical associations have formulated and published many engineering standards and codes within their respective fields. These have been developed under the procedure of the American Standards Association, Incorporated, and are published under its auspices as "American Standards."

21. *Standards within an individual factory.* The use of international, national, and industrial standards is an invaluable aid in the operation of the individual factory. However, each plant has problems peculiarly its own and requires individual standards to handle them. A list of some of these standards follows:

- (a) Standards of form and size.
    - (1) Machines of certain capacities.
    - (2) Wearing apparel forms and sizes, such as for shoes, coats, collars, etc.
- (b) Standards of quality or excellence of performance.
    - (1) Efficiency of boilers and engines.

Principles of Mass Production

   (2) Different grades of quality in manufacturing of shoes, clothing, etc.
   (3) Degrees of efficiency in the performance of machine operators.
(c) Standards of quantity.
   (1) The use of material in economic quantities.
   (2) The use of predetermined amounts of supplies under the budget system.
   (3) The amount of coal burned per kilowatt-hour.
(d) Standards of material.
   (1) Standard material specifications in scientific purchasing.
   (2) Different grades of materials purchased for the manufacture of different grades of products.
(e) Certain engineering standards.
   (1) Determination of standards of sizes and forms which are necessary for interchangeability.
   (2) Arriving at dimensional limits, tolerances and allowances.
(f) Standard methods of performing operations.
   (1) Operation standards in the use of correct sequence of operations.
(g) Standard performances in operations.
   (1) Meeting standards set by time and motion study.
(h) Standard conditions and tools in the performance of operations.

(1) Standards of temperatures and humidity for factory workers.

(2) Standards as to machine conditions, tight belts, sharp tools, etc.

The Ford Motor Company, for example, claimed that in the production of the Lincoln automobile more than 5,000 operations were performed in which the deviation from standard was not permitted to exceed one one-thousandth of an inch, while more than 1,200 operations were performed in which the deviation was not permitted to exceed one-half of one-thousandth of an inch. In the camshaft and crankshaft, the tolerances were held to one-quarter of one-thousandth of an inch, while in steel balls for ball bearings, the limit of tolerance was one ten-thousandth of an inch.

To produce such results certain master or reference gages are essential. So-called "block gages" are kept in the tool or gage departments, and these serve for checking and testing the thousands of individual gages of various types and sizes which are used on the shop floor.

22. *Advantages and disadvantages of standardization.* While standardization has advantages, there are also certain disadvantages. These may be briefly summarized as follows:

(a) *Advantages*
  (1) Reduction of costs through mass production.
  (2) Better quality through specialization.
  (3) Interchangeable parts.

(4) Decrease in clerical and engineering expense.
(5) Decrease in variety of stores, decrease in investments.
(6) Better deliveries.
(b) *Disadvantages*
(1) Difficulty and expense of changes to new styles and models.
(2) Tendency to retard progress because of inflexibility.

23. *Simplification.* A significant trend in recent years, affecting both the manufacturing and marketing activities of many organizations, is a movement toward the elimination of excess types and sizes. The term "simplification" has been given to this movement, and its activities were directed for a number of years by the Division of Simplified Practice of the United States Department of Commerce. As the result of its efforts, many types and sizes of various products were eliminated, with consequent savings of hundreds of thousands of dollars annually. A reduction from sixty-four types and sizes of paving brick manufactured to only four is a good example of its accomplishments in the direction of simplification.

In 1935, the Department of Commerce turned over this work to the American Standards Association in New York City. Since then, this Association has made notable progress in furthering the simplification movement.

Review

What is meant by "division of labor"?

Give examples of specialization in respect to the following: manufacturing; marketing; geographical locations; callings.

What are the advantages of specialization?

Explain "transfer of skill."

Show by an illustration the effect which an increase in output through the use of machinery has on unit cost.

What is meant by "standardization"?

Why is mass production dependent on the interchangeability of machine parts?

Into what four classes can standards be grouped from the standpoint of their scope?

What are the advantages and disadvantages of standardization?

What have been the results of efforts made in the direction of simplification in the matter of types and sizes?

CHAPTER VI

Line and Staff Control

1. *Organization.* Organization concerns itself with the classification or grouping of the activities of an enterprise for the purpose of administering these activities. Willis Rabbe, discussing the administrative organization for small manufacturing companies, in a paper in *Mechanical Engineering,* states that organization is to the business what the nervous system is to the human body. Its purpose is to send instructions (impulses) to the operating members, and to receive and transmit information to top management (the brain), so as to enable it to function intelligently.

Good management concerns itself with the development of people, as well as with the direction of things. This vital fact should always be kept in mind. Proper selection, training, and upgrading form the very basis of morale building, and morale can make or break an organization. In this chapter, however, attention is confined primarily to organization principles and practices as they are revealed in charts, records, procedures, and to other of the more mechanistic aspects of enterprise.

2. *Line organization.* Line or so-called "military" organization, the oldest and simplest form, is based upon

an exact division of duties, full authority, and discipline, which result in immediate obedience to instructions and precision in results.

Authority is passed down from the owners, through a board of directors, to a works manager. In the factory organization, a superintendent may head the manufacturing activities, and, in such a case, the foremen of the respective departments will report to him. Each department is, in most instances, a complete self-sustaining unit, its head being responsible for the performance of its particular process, product, or function.

Under such a setup, the foreman must (1) direct the technique, (2) formulate the necessary specifications, (3) obtain materials, (4) plan and schedule the work, (5) oversee the necessary handling of materials, and (6) keep the necessary cost and production records. The form of supervision is the same in all other departments, with complete control centered in each head, subject only to the will of the works manager. Any research, planning, or central record-keeping that is necessary, usually a small amount, is handled by the works manager. Figure 4 provides a simplified presentation of such organization.

A business controlled under the line form of organization may act more quickly and effectively in changing its direction and policy than any other form of organization. Line organization is very stable; ideas and orders travel strictly down the line of authority. There is never any question as to who is boss. Each

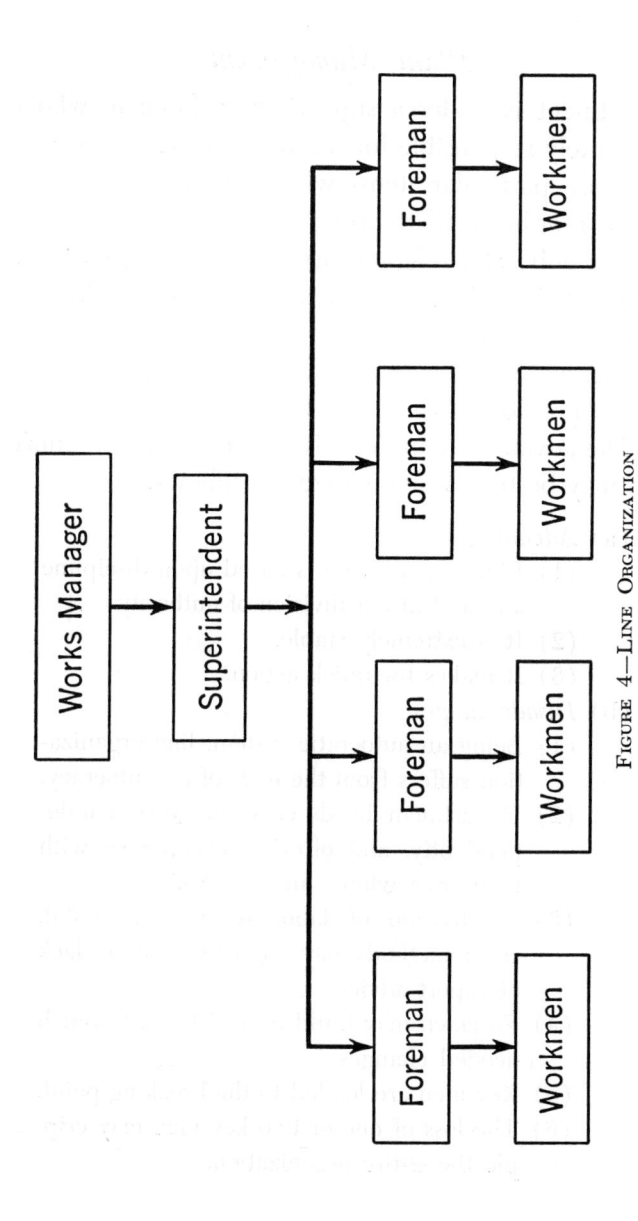

FIGURE 4—LINE ORGANIZATION

department is under a supervisor or foreman who is completely responsible for the work of the unit, except for those particular items which the works manager reserves for his own attention.

The only inter-relationship between the various departments is such as the works manager may establish. Thus, it is the works manager's duty to keep constantly in touch with all the details of the business, and to settle any problems that may arise.

The advantages and disadvantages of line organization may be briefly summarized as follows:

(a) *Advantages:*
    (1) Line organization is based upon discipline and a clear-cut division of authority.
    (2) It is extremely stable.
    (3) It makes for quick action.

(b) *Disadvantages:*
    (1) Being an autocratic system, line organization suffers from the evils of an autocracy.
    (2) Department heads carry out orders independently, and often in accordance with their own whims and desires.
    (3) As division of labor is only incidental, crude methods may prevail because of lack of expert advice.
    (4) Foremen may build up resistance to much needed changes.
    (5) Key men are loaded to the breaking point.
    (6) The loss of one or two key men may cripple the entire organization.

Line and Staff Control

The line relationship in modern management is important, although, because of its obvious limitations, there are few companies that operate entirely by line organization control.

3. *Line and staff organization.* In line and staff organization, the line serves to maintain discipline and stability, while the staff serves to provide expert advice. The importance of the line and staff method of control is readily appreciated by studying its relation to industry and business. The foreman or superintendent of a department neither has the time, nor is he usually capable, of making investigations, performing research work, or determining standards. Nevertheless, he is aware of the value of such things, and usually is glad to receive advice from someone who knows. The staff officers or services of an organization provide such advisory service, and carry on the following duties:

(a) Research into technical, operating, or managerial problems.
(b) Developing and recommending the various standards of performance.
(c) Keeping records and statistics as a means of controlling and evaluating performance.

These staff men have no direct authority either over line officers, or over the workers themselves. Any specifications, formulas, orders, or regulations which the staff departments recommend must have the approval of the president, general manager, works manager, or other coordinating officer to whom both the line and staff heads report. Line and staff organization is illustrated by Figure 5.

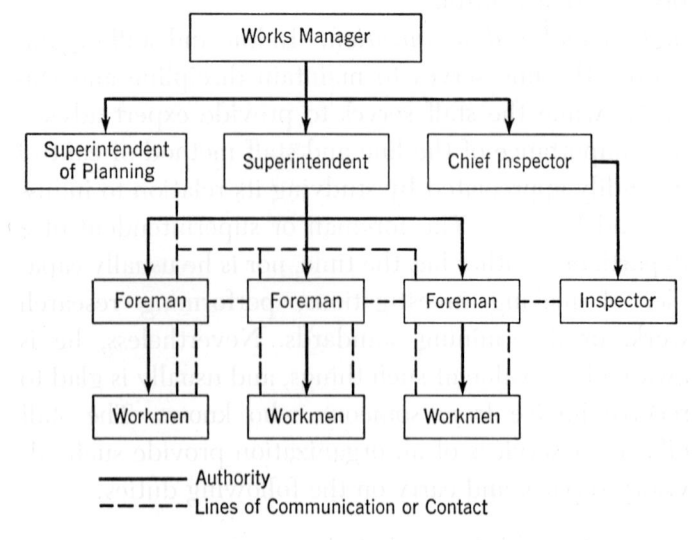

FIGURE 5—LINE AND STAFF ORGANIZATION

Line and staff control makes a clear distinction between doing and thinking—between the actual work of getting things done in the operating and other line departments, and the work of analyzing, testing, researching, accounting, and investigating carried on by the staff. It permits specialization by desirable functions, but, at the same time, maintains the integrity of the principle of undivided responsibility and authority.

The advantages and disadvantages of line and staff organization may be summarized as follows:

(a) *Advantages:*
  (1) Line and staff organization is based upon planned specialization.
  (2) It brings to bear expert knowledge.
  (3) It provides more opportunity for advancement for able workers, in that a greater variety of jobs is available.
  (4) It makes possible the principle of undivided responsibility and authority, and at the same time permits staff specialization.
(b) *Disadvantages:*
  (1) Line and staff organization may be ineffective for want of authority or intelligent backing.
  (2) The inability to see each other's viewpoint may cause difficulty and friction between the line and staff supervisors.
  (3) Although expert knowledge is available, it reaches the workers through line officers and therein lies the possibility of error and misinterpretation.

Because the technical nature of modern manufacturing requires the technical services best rendered by suitable staffs, line and staff organization is the most widely used in modern industry.

4. *Committee organization.* Where extensive use is made of committees in a company, committee organization constitutes the governing principle of the company. In general, such committees are supplementary to either line organization or line and staff organization.

Operations are carried on through directors' meetings, officers' meetings, and through committees appointed to supervise special activities.

The advantages and disadvantages of the use of committees may be summarized as follows:

(a) *Advantages:*
   (1) Under a strong executive chairman, a committee may quickly marshall many valuable points of view, since "two heads are better than one."
   (2) In conducting investigations, the several phases thereof may be quickly assigned to responsible members with a reasonable assurance of speedy action.
   (3) Decisions handed down by the chairman are impersonal, leaving him free from the personal criticism so often leveled at managing executives.
   (4) There is a stimulus toward cooperative action.
(b) *Disadvantages:*
   (1) Committees are expensive in time, usually cause delays, weaken individual responsibility, and make for compromise instead of clear-cut decisions.

5. *Executive committee.* The executive committee is the most important committee in a company which has a committee organization. Such a committee is likely to include the general manager, sales manager, works

manager, comptroller, chief engineer, purchasing agent and director of industrial relations. These men represent the various functions of executive power. No one of them alone can intelligently decide difficult questions of policy. When, however, the six men are assembled as an executive committee, each of the important functions is represented by an executive thoroughly familiar with his own field, and the discussions of such a body are likely to be wise and sound.

The general manager is logically the chairman of such a committee, and the matters that usually come before the committee pertain to the general policy of operating the plant. Thus, the committee might decide the character and size of the articles to be manufactured. It might approve all manufacturing orders for either stock or special products. It could decide all questions of extraordinary expenditures and could consider all economic problems of the plant.

6. *Equipment committee.* Where an equipment committee is appointed, it is usually made up of men drawn from different ranks. It may consist of the methods engineer, a representative of the superintendent's office, the foreman of the toolmakers, and any other men from the shop who may be of service. The chief engineer or his representative may also be included. If the plant employs an equipment manager, he is usually made the chairman of the committee.

Such a committee discusses all problems concerning new tools or improvement of existing equipment. When ways and means of reducing the cost of manufacture of any particular line of goods are under discussion, it is customary for the engineer who is familiar with the line to sit with the committee. An engineer, a good foreman toolmaker, and a good manufacturing foreman, together with the methods engineer, can often work wonders in reducing costs. A committee of this kind is also valuable in establishing standards and in advising the executive committee regarding the standardization of products.

7. *Production committee.* A committee composed of a few of the shop foremen and a representative from the production planning department, with the superintendent of manufacturing as chairman, is most effective in solving production problems. The duty of such a committee is to discuss all matters pertaining to the operation of the factory and the status of production orders, together with the reasons for any delays.

8. *Committee principles.* Whatever the function of a committee may be, it should be conducted on businesslike principles. Meetings should be called at regular intervals, careful minutes of the proceedings should be kept, and prompt attention given to all findings and recommendations.

The organization of committees, however, like all other instruments of management, should be handled with discretion and wisdom. The number and character of the committee that may be necessary will depend on the size and character of the plant. The committee

Line and Staff Control

system has limitations that must be observed for efficient operation. A committee that will be highly useful in one place may be useless elsewhere. In fact, especially in a small plant, a committee may be the cause of an actual waste of time.

Large enterprises sometimes resort to the committee system for coordinating a wide range of activities. This plan is advisable, particularly if the company operates a number of widely separated plants. The General Motors Corporation is an excellent example of an outstanding organization which has had exceptional success under this type of control.

9. *Multiple management.* Another type of managerial organization is that which is known as multiple management. Developed by Charles P. McCormick, president of McCormick & Co., manufacturer of a line of high-grade household food products, multiple management is provided by adding to the structure of a company certain extra units charged with responsible managerial duties.

One such unit is a so-called junior board composed of a certain number of men in charge of important office functions. The members selected are those who are rated by their peers as having contributed most to the company's efficiency during the previous six months' period. Each six months, three new members are elected to replace whichever three of the board are considered to have contributed least to the company's progress during the period. Displaced members may later regain membership in the board if, at any election period, they are among the three selected on the above merit basis. Other units in the multiple management plan are a factory board and a sales board. Members of these boards are selected along the same lines and under similar regulations as members of the junior board.

A member of the senior board of directors of the company is on each of these boards as a liaison representative of the senior board. All measures recommended by the auxiliary boards must have unanimous approval before they can be submitted to the senior board for ratification and put into operation.

During the two decades which have elapsed since McCormick & Co. put this multiple management into effect, it has been in successful operation in promoting the company's progress. Meanwhile, over 500 other companies have adopted the plan and have secured correspondingly gratifying results from its application.

10. *Modern trends in organization.* Lonnsbury S. Fish of the Standard Oil Company of California, in the *Ten Years' Progress in Management Report* of the American Society of Mechanical Engineers, lists the following recent trends in business organization:

  (a) Freeing top executives of administrative detail to concentrate on policy determination, long-range planning, and over-all control.
  (b) Decentralization of the burden of management by dividing and subdividing the enterprise into

its logical, separable components, each of which can be held fully responsible and accountable on a proprietary basis.
(c) Delegation or placement of the power of decision at the lowest practicable organization level, resulting in the elimination of unnecessary layers and levels of management, multiple handling, and "red tape."
(d) Better coordination and integration of staff functions.
(e) Clear-cut definition and understanding of the basic functions, objectives, relationships, and extent of authority for each principal position or agency.

Review

With what two basic factors does good management concern itself?

Describe line organization.

What are the duties of a foreman under line organization?

Name some of the advantages and disadvantages of line organization.

What is meant by line and staff organization and what are its advantages and disadvantages?

What are the advantages and disadvantages of committee organization?

What are the duties of the executive committee, the equipment committee, and the production committee?

Describe the type of managerial organization known as multiple management.

CHAPTER VII

The Works Manager as a Coordinator of Manufacturing Functions

1. *Basic elements in organization practices.* There are certain basic concepts or definitions which are constantly being used in the discussion of organization practices. Prominent among these are the terms: (a) duties, (b) authority, (c) responsibility, (d) power.

In his paper on "Scientific Principles of Organization," given before the American Management Association, L. Urwick, an English authority, defined these terms as follows:

> (a) *Duties,* in an organization sense, are the things an individual is required to perform because he occupies a certain position in an organization.
>
> (b) *Authority* is the right to require actions of other members of the organization. It varies, being
>> (1) Formal, that is, conferred by the organization.
>> (2) Technical, that is, implicit in special knowledge or skill.
>> (3) Personal, that is, conferred by seniority, popularity, or outstanding qualities of leadership.

The Works Manager as a Coordinator

(c) *Responsibility* is the accountability for the performance of duties.

(d) *Power* is the ability to get things done; in other words, it is a function of knowledge, skill, and personal qualities.

2. *Organization principles.* In the study of the subject of business organization, it is helpful to keep in mind certain general principles or laws applicable to all forms of organization. These may be stated as follows:

(a) *Principle of Purpose or Objective:*
  (1) All organizations and each part of any organization should be the expression of a purpose, either explicit or implied. (Urwick)
  (2) Each part and subdivision of the organization should be the expression of a definite purpose in harmony with the objective of the undertaking. (Alford)

(b) *Principle of Leadership:*
  Wise leadership is more essential to successful operation than extensive organization or perfect equipment. (Alford)

(c) *Principle of Authority and Responsibility:*
  (1) Responsibility for the execution of work must be accompanied by the authority to control and direct the means of doing the work. (Alford)
  (2) Formal authority and responsibility must be coterminous and coequal. (Taylor)

(d) *Principle of Ultimate Authority or Responsibility of Supervision:*
The responsibility of a higher authority for the acts of his subordinates is absolute. (Urwick–Alford)

(e) *Principle of the Scalar Chain:*
There must be a clear line of formal authority running from the top to the bottom of every organization. (Mooney and Reiley)

(f) *Principles of Exceptions:*
Managerial efficiency is greatly increased by concentrating attention solely upon those executive matters which are questions of policy, or are variations from routine, plan or standard. (Alford–Taylor)

(g) *Principle of the Span of Control:* (Number of subordinates who can be successfully directed by a superior.)
  (1) No superior can supervise directly the work of more than five or, at the most, six subordinates whose work interlocks. (Graicunas)
  (2) The number of subordinates reporting to a superior should preferably be limited to no more than five or six. (Alford)

(h) *Principle of Specialization of Function or Assignment of Duties:*
The work of every person in the organization should be confined, as far as possible, to the performance of a single leading function. (Taylor)

The Works Manager as a Coordinator

(i) *Principle of Coordination of Effort:*
The final object of all organizations is smooth and effective coordination. (Mooney and Reiley)

(j) *Principle of Homogeneity:*
An organization, to be efficient and to operate without friction, should bring together only duties and activities that are similar or are directly related. (Alford)

(k) *Principle of Definition:*
The duties, authority, responsibility, and relations of everyone in the organization structure should be clearly and completely prescribed in writing. (Taylor)

3. *Levels of authority and responsibility.* The degrees of authority and responsibility of an organization may be shown by drawing horizontal lines at the various executive levels. Thus, in Figure 6, the horizontal lines divide the chart into certain well-recognized levels of management as shown on the right of the diagram. These levels are: policy management, executive management, and supervisory management.

Policy management, often called "top management," determines the major policies or objectives of the organization, and serves as the governing authority. *Executive management* is responsible for carrying out the ideas of top management, with the works manager directing production; the sales manager directing sales; and the comptroller directing the accounting, cost accounting, clerical, and, perhaps, financial activities. This group works through the *supervisory management* which is composed of superintendents, foremen, and various key workers who are "translators of ideas into operation" in that they are in immediate contact with the actual producers.

A further division into levels of authority and responsibility is suggested by Urwick, according to which there are six levels as indicated on the left side of the diagram in Figure 6. They are as follows:

(a) Criticism and review—stockholders and stockholders' committees.
(b) Governing authority (administration)—board of directors.
(c) Liaison between policy and operation—the president.
(d) Operating authority—executive management (comptroller, works manager, sales manager).
(e) Supervision of operation—supervisory management (foremen and assistant foremen).
(f) Operation—the workers.

4. *Classification of activities: assignment of duties.* An organization chart may be divided further into vertical subdivisions as shown by the dotted vertical lines in Figure 6. Thus, the sales manager, the works manager, and the comptroller, each exercise authority within a certain field or range of control, subject to the higher authority of the president. In other words, the duties of each are carefully defined and prescribed. As a matter

The Works Manager as a Coordinator

Level	Structure	Management
1. Criticism and Review	Stockholders	POLICY MANAGEMENT
2. Governing Authority	Board of Directors / Chairman	POLICY MANAGEMENT
3. Liaison between Policy and Operation	President	POLICY MANAGEMENT
4. Operating Authority	Comptroller — Works Manager — Sales Manager	EXECUTIVE MANAGEMENT
5. Supervision of Operation	Superintendent of Manufacture / Foreman — Foreman — Foreman	SUPERVISORY MANAGEMENT
6. Operation	Workers	

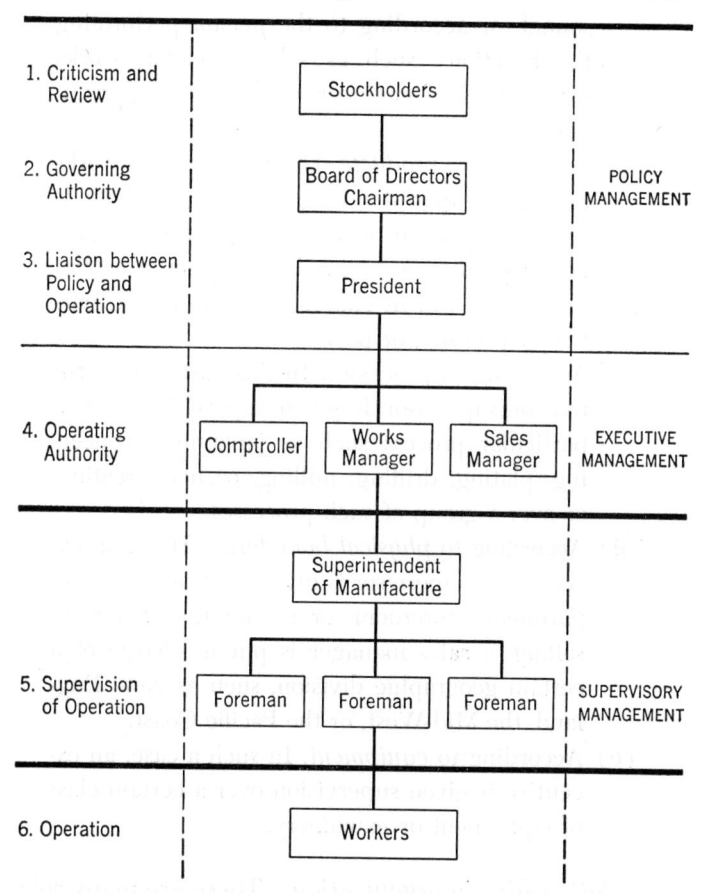

FIGURE 6—TYPICAL LEVELS OF AUTHORITY AND RESPONSIBILITY

of fact, duties or activities may be assigned in different ways. They may be assigned:

(a) According to the *functions* to be performed, such as selling, operating, engineering, or personnel; or according to the *person* performing the functions, such as sales manager, works manager, chief engineer, or director of personnel.

(b) According to *products*. This means that a works manager, superintendent, foreman, or boss is given supervision of the manufacture of a particular product, subassembly, or part; or a sales manager is put in charge of the sale of a particular product, or part.

(c) According to *processes*. In this case, an executive or supervisor is given supervision over a particular process such as japanning, veneering, plating, drilling, milling, or heat treating, or over a group of such processes.

(d) According to *physical boundaries*. Here, an executive or supervisor is given control over a department, storeroom, or production center. In selling, a sales manager is put in charge of a certain geographic division, such as New England, the Mid-West, or the Pacific Coast.

(e) According to *equipment*. In such a case, an executive is given supervision over a certain class of equipment or machinery.

5. *Relationships in organization.* There are many relationships in business organization, some of which cannot be shown on an organization chart. Among these many relationships are four in which management is principally concerned. These are: (a) line relationships, (b) lateral or cross relationships, (c) functional

The Works Manager as a Coordinator 109

staff relationships, and (d) general staff relationships.

6. *Line relationships.* Line relationships are those relationships between a superior and his subordinates immediately and directly responsible to him. Line positions are those directly responsible for the execution of the primary functions of an enterprise, namely, manufacturing and selling. Such relationships are generally of a formal nature.

7. *Lateral or cross relationships.* In any organization, there are certain recognized policies, orders, and instructions flowing from the top down. Flowing upward in return, there are reports, returns, suggestions, and recommendations. There may also be horizontal or cross-communication which involve the interchange of

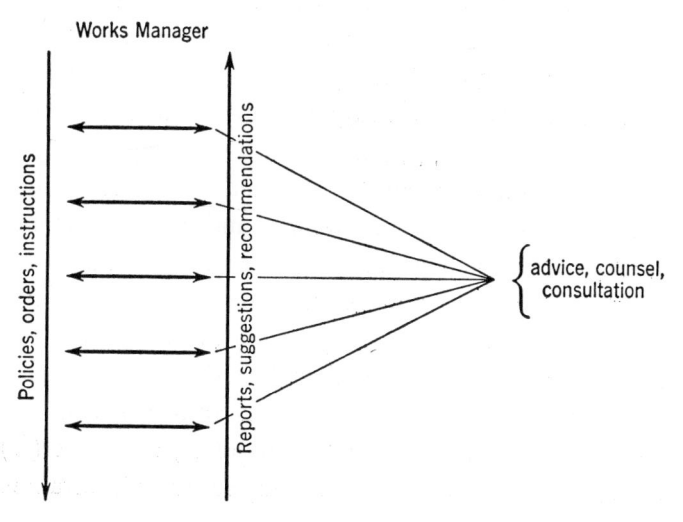

FIGURE 7—CROSS RELATIONSHIPS IN AN ORGANIZATION

advice, counsel and consultation. This is illustrated by the diagram shown in Figure 7.

In this diagram, the vertical line at the left represents the flow of policies, orders and instructions from the works manager down through the various departments under him. The vertical line at the right represents the upward flow of reports, suggestions and recommendations to the works manager. The horizontal lines represent the flow of communications between departments. This cross flow is a great timesaver. For example, when the foreman of the machine shop has a problem to discuss with the foreman of the foundry, he does so directly, although he afterwards reports the result of his conference to his immediate superior, the general foreman. If there were no provision for this cross-communication, the foreman of the machine shop would have to go up through the line to the works manager and then down through the line to the foreman of the foundry.

While cross-communications may save time, they may also be causes of conflict and friction. Henry Fayol, the French industrialist, recognizes this in his writings. He points out that the executives at any level in the line of authority may contact the one with another, reach decisions, and initiate action, provided that (a) the contact or relationship is initiated with the consent of the immediate line superior, and that (b) the approval of the immediate line superior is obtained before any action is taken.

8. *Functional staff relationships.* Certain positions, which are called staff positions, involve duties like providing expert advice or special counsel, and consequently involve relationships with other divisions of the organization. Since the term "staff" has thus taken on an additional meaning, it becomes necessary to speak of specialists or experts as the *functional* staff to distinguish them from the *general* staff.

9. *General staff relationships.* The term "general staff" comes from the army. It is concerned with the exercise of the authority at the highest level through assistants (aide-de-camps) who act for the chief executive, but without his direct knowledge or immediate consent. The functions of the assistant to the president are a good example.

10. *Executive control through coordination (principle of coordination of effort).* If a plan of organization is to be truly effective, it must be specific, clearly defining the duties of each individual, and coordinating every effort toward the ultimate objective. The duties of each executive, and the functions of every department, should be clearly stated in written form, with authority and responsibility definitely fixed.

The nature of the mechanisms coordinating executive control vary widely with different organizations and, for a particular establishment, they are generally known as its "system." System involves all forms of written and printed documents, such as organization charts, organization records, standard practice instructions, orders and returns, the records of all sorts, and the results of tests. In addition, it may cover managerial reports, and may include the transactions of committees and other bodies.

11. *Organization charts and organization manuals.* It is usually difficult to show anything but lines of authority upon the average organization chart. To attempt to show in addition the lines of communication would, in most instances, result in an unintelligible mass of lines. Even when the chart is limited to lines of authority, it may be complicated, since authority within certain fields may be overlapping.

To overcome these obvious defects of the organization chart, certain written instructions are formulated. These definitely state the authority, responsibilities, and duties of all members of the organization. Such documents are known as organization manuals and standard practice instructions. A typical works instruction sheet follows.

Duties of the Works Manager:
(a) He is responsible for the operation of the work in the manufacture of product for which capacity has been provided. In connection therewith he shall:
    (1) Produce apparatus and equipment of the quality defined by engineering specifications.
    (2) Produce in accordance with scheduled requirements.

The Works Manager as a Coordinator

(3) Operate in accordance with business methods prescribed in manufacturing department instructions.

(4) Operate to an approved budget.

(5) Establish loading rates (standard expense rates) in accordance with prescribed methods to return the expense to normal operation costs.

(6) Make all commitments for purchases which become a part of the works merchandise investment.

(7) Conform to standards of merchandise investment.

(8) Utilize labor in conformance with standard occupational classification.

(9) Employ incentive plans and establish piece rates for the remuneration of labor which conform to approved standards.

(10) Obtain functional approval for design or replacing equipment before purchase.

(11) Collaborate with the engineer of manufacture in launching manufacture of new products.

(12) Collaborate with the comptroller of manufacture in launching new business procedure.

(13) Collaborate with the engineer of manufacture in making periodic surveys of inspection methods and results.

(14) Operate facilities for constructing plant equipment as delegated by, or in fulfill-

ment of, orders and specifications from engineers of manufacture and plant.

(b) He is responsible for maintaining the works so that at all times it:
   (1) Has the prescribed capacity.
   (2) Is in satisfactory operating condition.
   (3) Provides maximum safety to employees.
   (4) Provides proper working conditions.
   (5) Conforms to the statutes governing industry.
   (6) Conforms to prescribed insurance regulations.

(c) He is responsible for the fullest application of the company's personnel relations policy. In connection therewith he shall:
   (1) Conduct training and educational activities to insure the greatest development of the individual employee's capabilities.
   (2) Up-grade employees along channels best suited to the development of the individual.
   (3) Promote appropriate out-of-hour activities for the education and recreation of employees.

(d) He is responsible for establishing wage scales for the standard occupational classifications of labor. In connection therewith he shall:
   (1) Make periodic wage surveys in the district of the works.

(e) He is responsible for the cost of the product. In connection therewith he shall:

The Works Manager as a Coordinator

(1) Be jointly responsible with the engineer of manufacture for the realization of estimated costs on new standard designs of product.

(2) Furnish the general commercial department with estimated costs of special products made on a jobbing or customers' order basis and of miscellaneous iron and wood work, cabling and special wired product for billing and contract purposes.

(f) He is responsible for operating and maintaining job shops and providing the special tool equipment required, for the manufacture of special products on a jobbing or customers' order basis.

(g) He shall install and rearrange manufacturing and service equipment in accordance with plans, prescribed standards and orders furnished or approved by the engineers of manufacture and plant. In connection therewith he shall:

(1) Store and dispose of manufacturing facilities no longer required.

(h) He is responsible for maintaining civic and commercial contacts, to insure for the works and its organization their proper place in the community and in industry.

12. *Standard-practice instructions.* An organization would be static if no one knew when, where, and how to proceed. Consequently, instructions are necessary,

and these are provided by written documents known as standard-practice instructions. These clearly define given procedures for accomplishing results from beginning to end. While there will usually be several ways to proceed in carrying out such a cycle, a "one best way" can be determined from experience, and this can be adopted as standard procedure.

13. *Orders and reports.* Written communications, with carbon copies for the information of all concerned, play a prominent part in modern management. Verbal orders are no longer used in well-managed plants. Records of a written nature are generally classified as orders or reports. Orders are instructions or directions coming from executives and departments. Reports record the carrying out of such orders, and give detailed information on the results of operation dealing with such factors as materials and labor. In other words, orders direct how work shall be done in the organization, while reports serve to record how the work has been performed.

14. *Records of performance.* Departmental executives cannot, and should not, handle the volume of detailed information contained in reports. Nevertheless, they must be kept informed of the performance of the various departmental operations. Consequently, records of performance, compiled by consolidating reports, are provided these executives for analysis. Recorded experience available for future planning is thus compiled in written form.

The Works Manager as a Coordinator

15. *Administrative reports.* Another form of document is compiled to provide the higher executives with an over-all picture of the entire factory. These administrative reports are prepared by consolidating the various departmental records.

16. *Coordination and control of functions.* The first duty of the works manager is to develop a means of organization whereby the functions under his direction can be properly differentiated and effectively set up. His next duty is to devise methods for putting these functions into action and controlling them, and he must accomplish the results required within the cost limits established. This means that he must coordinate performance so that bottlenecks will be avoided, departments will be kept busy, work will flow through to load the departments up to normal capacity, and the production of parts, subassemblies and assemblies will come along on schedule to meet shipping dates.

The kinds of activities which would normally be under the direction and control of the works manager are shown in Figure 8. The functions included are those which must necessarily be most closely coordinated in order to accomplish production on time, and to control both the doing and the cost of the work.

The grouping of these functions under one top executive, instead of dividing them among several such executives, makes possible the quick decisions necessary to keep production operations on an efficient, uninterrupted and low-cost basis.

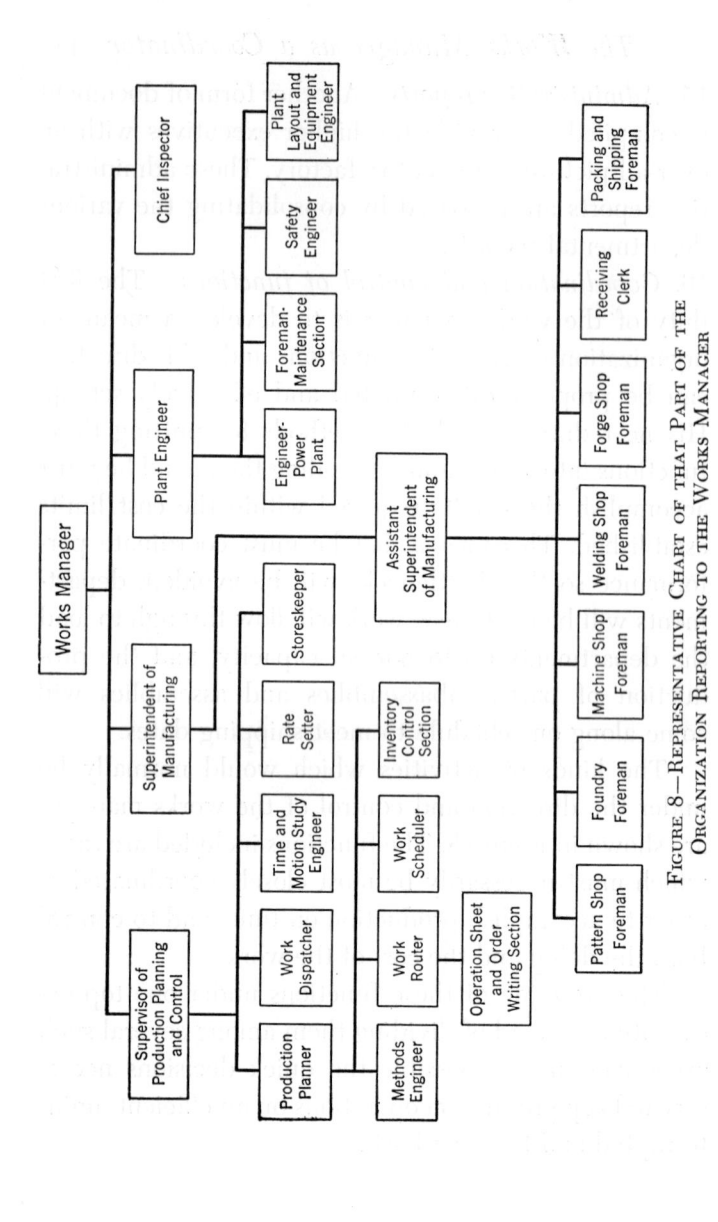

FIGURE 8—REPRESENTATIVE CHART OF THAT PART OF THE ORGANIZATION REPORTING TO THE WORKS MANAGER

The Works Manager as a Coordinator 119

17. *Techniques of coordination and control.* In securing coordination of work, it is necessary to determine first what has to be done, where it has to be done, when, by whom, and with what facilities and equipment. The next step is to determine the sequence relationships, with alternates wherever possible. These can be determined by methods studies and the preparation of operation sheets from which work-routing sheets can be prepared.

Scheduling is necessary to spot the operations in proper sequence on a manufacturing time table. The auxiliary services of time study and inventory control are needed to set up and keep such time tables. After that, proper dispatching must be worked out to put the plans into execution and bring the work through on time. This activity requires close coordination of the production-control and manufacturing departments. Plant engineering keeps power, maintenance work and plant layout coordinated for production planning and manufacturing performance.

Orders, production forms, reports and records are all necessary to coordinate and control all steps of the manufacturing cycle. While these should be kept as simple and as few in number as possible, nothing of importance should be left to memory. Otherwise, confusion, neglect and delays will result. Some works managers adopt and follow a comprehensive system of paper work, and rely on it to produce the desired results in volume and time of production. Others prefer fewer forms and more direct action, with some managers getting along with exceptionally simple set-ups.

The personality of the works manager is an important factor in acquiring proper coordination and control. If he is a leader, he stimulates his staff and workers to contribute heavily to the procurement of the results desired, and less paper work is required. Works managers who lack the quality of leadership, and rely on driving methods to push the work through, tend to defeat their own purposes by causing tensions, resistance and vindictiveness when team work and enthusiasm are needed in order to accomplish the desired results.

18. *Span of control.* The psychological concept of the span of attention places strict limits on the number of factors which the human mind can grasp simultaneously. It has its administrative counterpart in what is known as "Span of Control," which concerns the number of subordinates who can be successfully directed by one supervisor. Industrial-relations counselors point out that many labor disputes arise because the attempted span of control is too great. Where eight to twelve men may be successfully directed by a foreman, he frequently has fifteen to twenty under him. When too many subordinates are assigned to one superior, the result is likely to be delay, friction, confusion—in short, labor troubles.

Sir Ian Hamilton, writing on this subject in "The Soul and Body of an Army," says:

The Works Manager as a Coordinator

The average human brain finds its effective scope in handling from three to six other brains. If a man divides the whole of his work into two branches and delegates his responsibility, freely and properly, to two experienced heads of branches, he will not have enough to do. The occasions when they would have to refer to him would be too few to keep him fully occupied. If he delegates to three heads he will be kept fairly busy, whilst six heads of branches will give most bosses a ten-hour day. . . . As to whether the groups are three, four, five or six, it is useful to bear in mind a by-law: the smaller the responsibility of the group member, the larger may be the number of the group—and vice versa. . . . The nearer we approach the supreme head of the whole organization, the more we ought to work towards groups of three; the closer we get to the foot of the whole organization, the more we work towards groups of six.

Review

Define the following terms: (a) duties; (b) authority; (c) responsibility; (d) power.

Name eleven principles of organization.

Describe the three main levels of management.

Into what major classifications may the duties of the members of an organization be divided?

Name and describe the four relationships in business organization in which management is principally concerned.

What sort of documents does an organization's "system" involve?

Under what major heads do the duties of the works manager fall?

What is the purpose of standard-practice instructions?

Differentiate between "orders" and "reports."

How is coordination of work secured in an organization?

CHAPTER VIII

Production Planning and Control

1. *Control of production.* The activities of controlling production comprise the planning, routing, scheduling, dispatching, and inspecting functions in the productive process, with these functions so organized that the movements of materials, performance of machines, and operations of labor, however subdivided, are directed and coordinated as to quantity, quality, time and place. Thus, L. P. Alford, in *Principles of Industrial Management*, defines the activities which direct and regulate the flow of work through the plant.

It should be management's aim to control production in such a manner that the product shall be turned out by the *best* method, in the *shortest* time, at the *lowest* possible cost, and, at the same time, meet the quality requirements of the inspection department.

2. *Differences in control methods required.* In continuous-process and lot repetitive industries, where the raw materials enter one end of the factory and flow through in a continuous straight-line stream to the other, the production-control problem is relatively simple. The reason for this is that the paths or routes which the materials follow are fixed by the sequence

of processes necessary to make the product, while the *times* of the various operations are determined by the capacities of the machines and equipment. The frequency with which lots are sent through the factory is governed by the orders on hand, by the quantity of finished products in the stock room, and by the probable market demand.

3. *The need for accurate planning.* In the early days of factory management, the routing, scheduling, and dispatching of the product through the factory was left to the discretion of the foremen. The methods employed were based on the experience of these men, and, because of their manifold duties in many cases, the work was inefficiently performed. Under such methods, "stock tracers" and "chasers" were kept busy tracing and pushing the work through the factory.

Production planning and control departments have replaced these older methods, and their functions are to route or select the path, schedule the time, and dispatch or follow through on the performance of the work to keep it on schedule.

4. *The functions of routing, scheduling, and dispatching.* The functions of routing, scheduling, and dispatching work may be illustrated by considering the analogy between the operations of a factory and those of a railroad system. A train runs over a certain track, stopping at certain predetermined cities. This course has been laid out for the purpose of moving traffic between different stations, and is known as the route.

Production Planning and Control

The train is due to arrive at certain cities at certain times that are printed in the time tables. This is scheduling. At the various control points, the engineer looks for definite instructions or signals directing him to proceed from section to section. A dispatcher is responsible for the movement and control of the trains. This function is known as dispatching.

In a factory, a similar procedure is followed in carrying materials through to the finished product. This may be seen from Figure 9 which shows the schedule of a factory operating under a 5-day week with the first week starting on Tuesday because of New Year's Day falling on Monday. In processing a lot of machine parts, the routing, scheduling, and actual completion, or dispatching, of the successive operations was planned and performed as indicated according to the dates in the various columns. The final column for remarks is provided for recording causes of delays in dispatching. This column shows that the reason for the lot actually arriving at the finished stores department two working days late was a breakdown on drill press No. 53.

5. *Handling a sales order.* Planning, especially in the intermittent or job shop type of industry, usually begins with the receipt of a sales order. A sales order is first passed for customer's credit by sending it to the credit department, frequently a unit in a controller's division. Then, the order is accepted by acknowledgment to the customer, provided that the order is for

PLANNED OPERATION SHEET
Schedule

Oper. No.	Routing	Arriving	Leaving	Actually Dispatched	Remarks
1.	Planner Department	January 2	January 4	January 4	
2.	Horizontal Boring Mill	January 5	January 10	January 12	
3.	Milling Machine Department	January 11	January 15	January 17	Breakdown on drill press No. 33
4.	Drill Press Department	January 16	January 17	January 19	
5.	Finished stores	January 18		January 23	

FIGURE 9—PLANNING SHEET FOR CONTROLLING PROGRESS OF WORK

Production Planning and Control

standard items, or, if not, that an estimate and quotation have previously been made and the customer is now placing the order.

If the order is one in which the goods can be shipped from stock, procedure from then on is a simple matter. A shipping order is written and sent to the finished products stock room. The goods are then delivered by the stock room to the shipping department which sends the goods to the customer, who is billed in the usual manner.

If, however, the order is for an article not in common use, but is a special item, such as a machine repair part, or some other product requiring a careful check to assure the proper filling of the order, the order needs to be approved by the engineering or product design department as one that can be filled from stock. In case such a department finds that the item required is not in stock, it works out the specifications for its manufacture or assembly. When products have to be manufactured specifically to order, the planning and control of production involves a far greater amount of work than the amount of work which is required in the manufacture of standard items.

If an order is for several different items made by different branches of a company's manufacturing division, it is broken down into separate manufacturing orders, one for each type of product. This breakdown is either made at once in the sales division or, later, in the manufacturing division.

128 *Plant Management*

6. *Putting an order into production.* Copies of a production order go to the following divisions of a manufacturing organization:

   (a) The sales division's staff, for recording and the follow-up of manufacturing and shipping.
   (b) The engineering division for design of the product.
   (c) The production planning and control division, for the planning and follow-up of all activities to put the order through production.
   (d) The manufacturing division for production of the product.
   (e) The shipping department. It is necessary for this department to enter the order on the shipping docket so as to be ready to pack and box, crate, or palletize the product as soon as it comes from the production lines, and to have cars, trucks, or barges if the plant is on the waterfront, ready to transport it at once to the customer.

7. *Typical production control procedure.* As an illustration of production control procedure, assume that a customer's order has been received by the *sales division* of a manufacturing plant. This order is first approved by the credit department, and forwarded to the production planning and control, the engineering, and the shipping departments.

The *production planning and control department* gives copies of the order to its planning section and its

Production Planning and Control

methods section. These sections then simultaneously start work. As soon as the nature of the order as to manufacturing requirements, and its possible position on the production schedule can be determined, an estimated completion and shipping date is given to the head of the production control department. If he finds this date can be met, he immediately informs the manufacturing division head and the sales department of the date when the customer may expect shipment. This information is then communicated to the customer from the sales department.

Meanwhile, the *engineering division* begins work so as to release design data, drawings, specifications, bill of materials, drawing lists, parts and pattern numbers, and any other necessary information as soon as possible to the production control department. Much of this information can often be sent along early so as to facilitate getting the order under way.

Upon receipt of the bill of materials, the *production planning section* at once sends a copy to the stores records section. This latter section promptly checks all the items which are carried in stores, and indicates those which are not carried. It then requisitions replenishments of any needed items—either raw materials or parts—which are low in stock.

When the marked bill of materials is returned to the planning section, purchase requisitions are made out and forwarded to the purchasing department for all items which must be obtained from the outside. In the case of stored parts made up from the company's raw materials, the inventory clerk, if stocks are low, files requisitions with the production planning section, which then puts through manufacturing orders to make up a supply of the necessary parts from the raw materials.

As soon as possible, the *methods section* analyzes all drawings, specifications, and the like, for the purpose of developing the best manufacturing procedures for filling the order. This section often confers with the engineering department during the course of design so that the parts which are to be made in the plant may be produced so far as possible by the existing machinery, fixtures, tools and other facilities of the plant, and thus keep the cost for changes and new equipment down to a minimum.

While all this is going on, any required *time and motion study* data are assembled or developed so as to set standard times and provide the basis for writing-up instruction cards for the operators on the various jobs. A large amount of information on job times may be derived from carefully recorded, defined and classified data on previous jobs with the same or similar detailed work elements. Consideration is also given to the matter of wage rates which are stated or worked out by the rate-setting section for all operations involved under the order.

Work simplification is regularly carried on by progressive plants for the purpose of (a) improving job

Production Planning and Control

procedures, (b) establishing efficient workplace layouts, (c) simplifying or better adapting the tools and equipment used for performing the necessary operations, and (d) training foremen and workers in methods improvements for the most efficient production. Accomplishments in work simplification result from the experienced application of the refined technics of time and motion study to eliminate useless steps and motions in doing work.

Processing analysis is also carried on in preparing to fill an order, and this results in the specifying of the tools and fixtures needed for the jobs, and in the initiating of orders for tool design and manufacture or purchase, where manufacturing costs can be cut by new tooling. Equipment data are consulted or collected to determine what machinery is to be used for the various operations or processes required by the order. Finally, manufacturing procedures are set for all the jobs under the order, and operation sheets are written. When these sheets used in connection with the *specific manufacturing order* in question, they become "route sheets" by filling in the specific order number, quantities of parts to be produced, and other pertinent facts.

A considerable amount of the above kind of information needed for jobs handled by the average company is maintained on file by the company, and this generally covers a large percentage of the company's orders for standard products made from standard parts. In fact, much of this information is kept in such shape that it can be applied to a new order with little change outside of the insertion of the order number and the quantity going through on the order. Where the information does not exactly apply to an order, there are usually sufficient data on record under various classifications to permit the required times, operation sheets, and the like, being built up synthetically.

Once all the data are assembled which are needed to put an order through, the *order-writing unit* of the planning section, from the information thus supplied, fills out the final forms required by the order, such as time cards, material issue slips, inspection tickets, move tickets, and identification tags. In filling out these forms, as well as in preparing many other forms and data sheets used in production control, wide use is made of highly efficient time-saving and cost-saving equipment.

The forms and papers prepared for the filling of an order are sorted and assembled according to the respective detailed operations to be performed. They are then filed in a central dispatch office, together with the drawings and the paper work developed by the methods section of production control.

8. *Procedure in issuing and accounting for materials.* To assure that no slip-up is made in regard to supplies, such as materials and parts, on hand in the storeroom for the filling of the order—their availability having been determined through use of a copy of the bill of materials—the following procedure is adopted:

Production Planning and Control

(a) As soon as the materials issue slips are written in the planning or order-writing section, they are sent to the stores-records section for pre-posting in the "apportioned" columns of the individual stores-record sheets, and are deducted from the "available" columns. The stores-records clerk initials each slip to show that it has been thus posted. Consequently, in checking any subsequent orders calling for such materials, there will be no danger of promising the *same* materials to these later orders.

(b) The stores-issue slips are then filed with the work order to which they apply in the central dispatch office of the production control division.

(c) When the time approaches for the order to be processed in the plant, the materials issue slips, and the other papers covering the job, are sent to the local dispatch station in the manufacturing department where the work is to be done. This station is usually in or near the foremen's office.

(d) When the order is about to be processed in the department, and the materials are needed, the materials-issue slips are presented to the proper storeroom.

(e) The stores clerk supplies the materials, has the slips signed by the recipient, and subtracts the quantities from any bin tags or stores records kept in the storeroom, and the materials are delivered by either the storeroom delivery service or the plant industrial truck system.

(f) The storeskeeper then initials the slips and sends them to the stores-records section where they are deducted from the "balance-on-hand" column and the "apportioned" column, the latter entry thus cancelling the previous apportionment.

(g) Often the stores-records section carries cost data on each kind of item, in which case the unit cost—and sometimes the total value—of the materials issued is entered on the material-issue slips. The slips then go to the cost department.

(h) In the cost department, the values are entered on a materials-cost sheet for the production order to which they apply.

(i) They may also be entered on a summary-of-materials-issued form.

(j) Afterwards, the slips are sent to the accounting department where they are sorted and posted to the work-in-process account as a credit, and to the raw-materials account as a debit.

(k) They are filed temporarily in this arrangement, but are finally destroyed after any data of value for future use has been extracted from them.

(l) In the meantime, the materials received from the storeroom are checked and sent to the machine or work areas where they enter into the manufacturing process.

9. *Routing and scheduling of work.* Concurrent with the procedures which thus far have been described, the various parts to be made and assembled are routed according to the plan of manufacturing laid out on the respective operation sheets. The flow of work is thus determined and, in the case of many companies, flow

charts are drawn to show the course of the work. These charts are then studied from time to time to see where changes in work routes, combinations of operations, and even changes in the actual layout of equipment, can cut down the travel of materials and the time required to get the work done.

Scheduling of the work accompanies routing. Previous orders already under production will have loaded up the plant equipment and facilities to a certain extent and the new work to be scheduled will have to fit in with the program already in operation. Rush work may cause some changes to be made in previous plans to get an important order through in a hurry. On the other hand, certain departments and machines may be partially idle at the time, and will be for periods in the immediate future, because of a lack of orders sufficient to keep them going.

Into this picture the new work going through is fitted, operation by operation, to make maximum possible use of all manufacturing facilities at the earliest date when machines will be available. Some parts on a new order, therefore, may be put into immediate production on idle equipment, although the parts will not be needed for a considerable time. Other parts, perhaps, cannot be scheduled to be produced when desired under the planning, unless work already assigned to the machines and work centers involved is moved to some other date.

Sometimes, such re-scheduling is possible without

affecting final delivery of the earlier orders for which the parts are being made. In other cases, the earlier orders, if moved to a later date on the schedule, will fall behind promised delivery dates unless overtime work is done. Overtime work, however, is costly, usually undesirable, and sometimes impossible procedure, as in cases where two-shift or three-shift operation is already in effect. It is then necessary to decide which order—the old or the new—takes precedence, and to act accordingly.

When a good production planning and control system is efficiently operated, questions of this kind are reduced in number because a manufacturing concern is usually aware of what the situation is when it accepts a new order. Consequently, the concern can arrange it so that the promised delivery date on the new order does not interfere with the date of the old order.

It is considered advisable to fill up all open gaps in the current work schedule by assigning new work for those vacant periods, even though this results in new work being done considerably ahead of time. Then, if unexpected orders are received later, they can be accepted and put through more readily. Furthermore, if any shifts in the current scheduling are necessary, they can be made without actually delaying the current orders.

In building up a schedule, it is considered to be good practice to leave no "cushion" time between orders to take up slack, except the allowances provided for in the actual time studies. Furthermore, any such extra allowance time should be pooled at the end of work periods, say Friday of each week, or at longer intervals. Otherwise, allowances usually degenerate into "required" time, causing a relaxing of schedules, and consequently a cutting-down of production far below plant possibilities. If the extra time provided at the end of specified periods is not needed to bring delayed work into line, future work can be moved back into the period, or some new work can be put into production.

10. *Mechanisms for production control.* Before outlining the procedures used in dispatching orders through manufacturing, it seems advisable to consider the mechanisms employed in production control for work planning, machine loading, scheduling, and regularly and consistently following up on the progress of work.

The general classes of mechanisms used for such purposes are as follows:

(a) Production control boards or mechanical systems.
(b) Visible index or card systems.
(c) Gantt charts.
(d) Graphical card-insert systems.
(e) Punched card and tabulating machine systems.
(f) System for duplicating work orders and other forms.
(g) Communication systems.

Gantt Charts lend themselves readily to illustration, to general application, and to dynamic control over all kinds of work activities. Some of the other systems, in fact, constitute mechanical Gantt Charts. Punched card and tabulating machine systems offer the widest opportunity for rapidly recording, sorting, compiling, calculating and applying production information in connection with an unlimited amout of production-control data.

11. *Dispatching work.* In a small plant, the central dispatch office does all of the local dispatching of work. In large companies, there is often a local dispatch station in each important department, including maintenance and other units which operate under work schedules.

12. *Placing the order on the planning and dispatch boards.* The central dispatch clerk has charge of the planning board or other mechanism used for controlling manufacturing operations. From this central control station, he regulates the work scheduling at the several departmental dispatch boards. In many cases, a summary of work scheduled for a forthcoming period is developed in advance for each department and sent to the various foremen. They can thus do some preliminary local planning.

In advance of the work periods, the folders or envelopes containing the data for each job are sent to the respective local dispatch stations. Here, the local dispatcher assists the foreman by doing all the miscellaneous preparation and paper work necessary to get the orders lined up for actual production. When such work as this is left entirely to the foreman, it greatly hampers him in getting production out.

When the local dispatcher receives the work folder or file for a given machine or product, he takes out and retains the route sheets or planned operation lists until the jobs are completed in his department. These sheets show the general sequence or course of the work, but they are not needed for direct use at any of the work stations.

The local dispatcher then lines up each operation to be performed and, at the direction of the foreman, assigns the work to the kind of machine or production center to which it has been routed. He usually does so by removing the duplicate work order, and other duplicate documents necessary for complete identification and control of the operation, and placing them on the planning board upon the hooks, or in the pockets, controlling the particular machine to which the work is assigned.

The operation envelope, with its remaining duplicate contents, is filed in the department until the particular machine or processing job to be done there is completed. The local dispatch clerk does this for each operation to be done in his department, and for which he has received operation envelopes, placing the work orders so that they are in the sequence called for by the scheduled time of performance.

13. *Getting the work on the machine.* Assume, for example, that the first of these machines, or processes to which work has been so assigned, is a Jones and Lamson turret lathe No. 50. Assume, furthermore, that there is plenty of work ahead of the machine so that this particular work order and its related instructions must be placed in proper sequence in the upper or "jobs-ahead" pocket of the planning board. In due course of time, the envelope will be advanced to the second, or "next-job," pocket. If there is a master control board in the department, corresponding changes will be made upon this departmental dispatch board.

When the work order has been advanced to this "next-job" position, the dispatch clerk takes the materials-issue form from the operation envelope, if materials are to be drawn from the stores, and gives them to the trucker or move man. He also gives him the identification tags that are to be fastened to the work, all of which bear the identification numbers. The move man, with this authority, draws the materials, signs the materials-issue slip, and returns it to the stores clerk. He then tags the materials and moves them to the machine.

The dispatch clerk also issues the tool, fixture, jig or other equipment orders to the move man. With these as authority, the move man procures from the tool crib all special tools and appliances needed, and brings them to the machine in advance of the beginning of operations.

Production Planning and Control

A special set-up man, or the workman himself, if there is no set-up man, removes any tools which are on the machine, and replaces them with the tools for the new job, thus getting the machine ready for the work. He may put through and inspect a trial piece to see that the machine is properly set. The move man then takes the tools from the previous job back to the tool crib and reclaims the checks or tool slips deposited when the tools were taken out for the previous job.

14. *Completing the work.* Now assume that the operator assigned to do the new job on Machine No. 50 has finished the job on which he was previously working, and is ready to go on this new job. He takes the operation order, instruction card, time card, and other sheets from his previous job to the dispatch station, and returns them to the dispatch clerk, who stamps the time upon the time card.

The dispatch clerk now takes from the work-in-process pocket the duplicate documents pertaining to the work which this man has just completed. At the same time, he advances the corresponding documents of the new job to the work-in-process position for Machine No. 50. He stamps the time upon the time card for this new order and gives the card to the workman, with the work order, instruction card, and other sheets, for the new operation.

The workman then goes to Machine No. 50 and starts the new operation for which complete preparation has been made. The dispatch clerk at the same time issues the new inspection orders to the inspector who is to be responsible for checking the work on Machine No. 50.

The move man takes the work previously completed on Machine No. 50 to the next machine listed on the route sheet, and also as stated above, returns to the tool crib all tools and fixtures used on the job just finished. The dispatch clerk returns all such matter as work orders, drawings, and drawing lists on this previous job to the central dispatch clerk, who enters a record of the completed operation on the master planned operation list, and clears his own control board of this finished operation.

The completed time cards are sent to the payroll department where they are first checked against the attendance-board record or time-clock record of the various workers, and are then used in making up the payroll. They are later forwarded to the cost department where, with the materials-issue slips, they form the basis for calculating the production costs on the work.

The foregoing discussion describes the complete plan of production control based on Taylor's methods, and is basically typical of all such plans now in actual use. Wherever possible, paper-work procedures on jobs are simplified and forms are reduced to the minimum. Modern duplicating, tabulating and work-control equipment cut out or shorten many of the detailed steps formerly done by hand methods.

Production Planning and Control

Review

What should management aim to accomplish through control of production?

Explain the manufacturing functions of routing, scheduling, and dispatching.

To what five divisions of a manufacturing organization are copies of a production order sent?

Summarize the procedure in issuing and accounting for materials.

What are some of the problems involved in scheduling new work?

Name the general classes of mechanisms used in production control.

Outline the procedure in the dispatching of work.

CHAPTER IX

Purchase, Control and Storing of Materials

1. *Purchasing and its place in industry.* Because of the increasing influence of purchasing in industry, the tendency is to elevate the position of the purchasing department in the organization, and to make the purchasing agent a member of the committee on general administration. In a growing number of cases, he is made a vice-president of the company. When it is realized that the purchasing agent's expenditures for materials, supplies and equipment amount to from 35 to 55 per cent of the total cost of manufacturing a company's product, the importance of his position is at once recognized.

2. *Purchasing policies.* There are various means by which a sound, alert purchasing organization can accomplish much in reducing the cost of materials and supplies. For example, it can regulate the time of purchase so as to take advantage of favorable markets. It can purchase in quantity so as to gain the advantage of quantity discounts. It can pay bills promptly so as to obtain cash discounts, and finally, it can devise methods of purchase so as to protect the company from disastrous commitments, excessive inventories, and unnecessary crowding of storage space.

Purchase, Control and Storing Materials 145

The experienced purchasing agent knows how to resist the temptation to overbuy when apparent bargains appear on the market. To help guard against this danger, the financial department, in fixing its financial budget, can see to it that the materials budget is definitely planned. This precaution will control the expenditures for each particular line of materials, but will not prevent taking advantage of unusual opportunities for favorable purchases of material if they present themselves. In the case of such opportunities, arrangements can be made to have any extra expenditures authorized by some higher authority so that purchases of this kind can be made.

3. *Legal factors.* Purchase orders when acknowledged by vendors become binding contracts upon buyer and seller. Obviously, they should be in written form. In fact, most states require that orders amounting to more than fifty dollars, to be valid, must be in writing. This means that the purchasing agent should have a working knowledge of business law, and be familiar with the provisions of the Law of Agency, the Law of Contracts, and other branches of legal practice. Since he is recognized as the buying agent of his company, his acts commit the company to carry through the transactions covered by purchase orders.

4. *Centralized vs. localized purchasing.* Centralized purchasing in a plant offers the following advantages over localized purchasing by individual departments or factories:

(a) The buying records are all located in one department under single supervision.
(b) There is one place where visiting sales representatives are interviewed.
(c) Time is saved by the visiting salesmen.
(d) Purchases are combined and quantity discounts secured.
(e) Blanket contracts can be negotiated for a considerable period in advance to protect prices and make sure of deliveries.
(f) Vendors secure larger orders, thus cutting their manufacturing and selling expenses and making it possible for them to quote lower prices.
(g) Varieties of items bought may be reduced to a minimum and standards set.
(h) Inventories are reduced.
(i) Standardization of materials and reduction of inventories cut the costs of purchasing and storing.

5. *Place of the purchasing department in the organization.* The relative location of the purchasing department in the factory organization depends on the size of the factory and its purchasing policies. In small plants, for financial and clerical reasons, this department may be placed directly under the comptroller or the treasurer. In factories of medium size, it is usually placed under the direction of the general manager. In very large organizations, there is usually a central purchasing organization under a general purchasing agent, who may be a vice-president of the company, with a local

Purchase, Control and Storing Materials 147

purchasing agent in each plant to look after the buying of materials parts and supplies special to that plant.

6. *The purchasing agent.* A representative list of the duties of the purchasing agent has been presented in a pamphlet published from the results of a study by the Policyholders Service Bureau of the Metropolitan Life Insurance Company. These duties are as follows:

- (a) The purchasing agent buys all materials and services required by the company, and is responsible for these until they are delivered to the consuming department.
- (b) He studies business conditions and markets.
- (c) He investigates new materials and equipment.
- (d) He establishes relations with suppliers and investigates possible new sources of supplies.
- (e) He disposes of obsolete material and equipment.
- (f) He is responsible for keeping the raw materials inventory at the lowest possible figure consistent with business and market conditions.
- (g) He interviews salesmen who call personally, and puts them in touch with the technical men of the organization. In addition, the study of sales literature received is part of his duty.
- (h) In a number of companies, the purchasing agent is responsible for traffic work to the extent of filing claims and securing such adjustments as are necessary as a result of the receipt of goods damaged in transit.
- (i) In many companies, the purchasing agent as-

148 *Plant Management*

sists the company's personnel in personal purchases and procuring special discounts for them.

7. *Responsibilities of the purchasing department.* The purchasing department of the manufacturing plant is charged with important responsibilities. Materials must be kept coming in so as to flow through production in the volume necessary to meet manufacturing schedules on time, but not at such a rate as to result in the building up of large and costly inventories. The cycle of duties involved in the placing of each of these orders includes most, and often all, of the following steps:

(a) A request or authorization is received to buy materials, supplies or equipment.
(b) The request is checked to find out what is wanted, and in what volume the purchase should be made.
(c) A study is made of current prices, discounts, and supplies on the market.
(d) Files, catalogs or buyers' guides are consulted to locate possible suppliers.
(e) Requests for quotations or bids are sent out.
(f) Bids or offers are analyzed to select a vendor whose quality, delivery, service and price on the commodity desired is the most favorable.
(g) Follow-up is made on important orders to check on their delivery in satisfactory shape on the scheduled date, or before.
(h) The items are checked on arrival, adjust-

ments are made for any shortages or other errors, the invoice is paid, and the purchasing and accounting records are cleared on the order.

8. *Purchase requisitions.* The materials purchased for most enterprises are of two classes: (a) direct materials which are to go into the product; (b) indirect materials and supplies, such as coal, brooms, and oil, which do not become a part of the product itself, yet are chargeable against production.

In plants manufacturing standardized products, most purchase requisitions originate with the inventory control section, since it is the function of this section to keep the factory supplied with materials regularly carried in stores. When materials are needed by the operating departments, a materials requisition is sent to the storeskeeper. The production planning department usually makes out purchase requisitions for items not regularly carried in stores.

In case of a shop which does jobbing or repair work and the material needed for each job is usually different, the storeroom may handle only indirect materials or supplies. In such a case, purchase requisitions for direct materials originate largely with the production planning department, or with a foreman or the superintendent in the absence of such a department.

If a factory is getting ready for new work, involving the preparation of drawings and engineering requisitions, the purchase requisitions originate in the production planning department if there is one; otherwise they originate in the engineering department. If the materials or parts needed are highly specialized, the specifications and perhaps the requisitions are made out in the engineering department.

9. *Requisitions from several sources.* In plants which are so organized that requisitions for the purchase of materials may originate from several sources, care needs to be taken that only duly appointed officials are given authority to make out requisitions for goods of any kind. Furthermore, no matter where the requisition may originate, it should pass through the hands of the inventory control man or the storeskeeper so that he may use whatever materials he may have on hand, or use up other materials that may be substituted.

The purchase requisition in all cases should bear all the information needed to identify the materials with the work or purpose for which they are intended.

10. *Importance of specifications.* Specifications for the purchase of simple standard articles may be, and often are, prepared by the purchasing department. As a general thing, however, specification writing is not a function of the purchasing agent. This is particularly so where engineering principles or scientific data must form the background of the specifications.

If an article to be purchased is a proprietary or patented one, the specifications may be very simple, for little doubt can exist in such a case as to what is required. Where competitive bids are asked before

Purchase, Control and Storing Materials

placing an order, the case is very different. Here care should be taken that all bidders are informed as to exactly what is wanted. The specification should describe the article so clearly as to form, quantity, and characteristics as to permit of no ambiguities or misunderstandings.

The specification should also be explicit as to all business relations, time of delivery, and the inspection tests that are to be applied. When such inspection tests are specified, they should be scrupulously carried out.

11. *Economies possible through specifications.* The purchasing agent can often make considerable savings by standardizing articles of common use that are required by several departments. All ordinary supplies, such as paper, envelopes, pens, pencils and furniture used in the offices, and many articles used in common by the factory departments, such as bar stock, bearings and gears, can be standardized, This makes it possible to purchase such articles in much larger quantities and, consequently, at lower prices than would otherwise be the case.

In large plants where the variety of materials needed is great, a department known as a materials department is sometimes organized. Such a department assumes full responsibility for the quality of the material needed, and carries out such inspection and tests as may be necessary to insure this quality.

Wherever possible, specifications should contemplate the purchase of stock materials, or articles readily available in the open market. Special materials or articles should be called for only when absolutely necessary. When special materials must be specified, the amount purchased should be sufficient for only the work in hand. The reason for this is that such materials depreciate in value very rapidly when left unused in stores.

A specification for a piece of apparatus, such as a motor, is adequate if it covers type, size, capacity, and performance, without going into minute details of construction that may not be vital. The purchasing agent is thus allowed some latitude in placing the order, since he is not limited by the specifications in the matter of details, nor is he prevented from resorting to the substitution of materials if necessary. In the case of substitution, however, it is usually advisable for him to consult the person issuing the requisition as to taking such action.

In case specifications are detailed, they often allow for a certain stated amount of deviation, substitution, or tolerance. This not only helps the purchasing agent, but it frequently enables the seller to quote a much lower price than if he had to supply the exact size called for by the specification.

12. *Purchase records.* If the number and variety of articles to be procured is very large, some systematic method needs to be followed in keeping currently informed on sources of supply. It is not sufficient to trust to trade catalogs alone. Changes in list prices of manu-

facturers from whom purchases can be made are frequent, and new producers coming into the market may offer superior facilities and lower prices. Some markets are narrow, making it important to collect and tabulate data bearing upon them. Such data will keep the purchasing agent informed at all times as to where he can obtain the required quality of materials at the lowest price.

13. *Receiving and inspecting.* Provision should always be made for inspecting purchases at the time they are received, both as to quantity and quality. In small plants, this may be accomplished by placing the receipt and inspection of all purchased material in the hands of some one person or department specifically charged with these duties. In large plants, a well-organized department for receiving and inspecting incoming shipments is essential. Such a department is usually organized as an independent function, and is permitted to operate in this capacity.

Mechanical inspection is usually employed to determine the accuracy of size. In inspecting for quality, mechanical or chemical tests may be necessary. This work may be so important as to require a special testing laboratory. Small concerns that cannot afford elaborate equipment for complete mechanical and chemical tests can often engage the services of commercial laboratories that do work of this character.

14. *Stores and stocks.* There is a definite trend toward standardization in the use of the terms "stores" and

"stocks." Unworked materials are usually referred to as "stores," while the place where they are kept is known as the storeroom. Finished products that are ready for shipment are usually called "stock" and are housed in a place called the stock room.

Under ideal conditions, raw materials would be used as fast as they arrived at the factory, going through the various manufacturing operations, and being shipped to customers as fast as they were converted into the finished product. Storerooms and stock rooms would be unnecessary under such conditions. These conditions can only be approached, however, and then only in simple repetitive-flow or continuous process industries.

15. *Necessity for storerooms and stock rooms.* In a large majority of factories, raw materials are used in varying amounts, at varying times, and for a market that is varied and intermittent. Because of this fact, and also because economical purchasing and transportation usually involve large quantities, space must be provided for the storing of incoming materials, which are drawn out as the manufacturing departments need them.

To insure prompt delivery to customers in a varying sales market, products are frequently manufactured in advance of sales. Provision must be made, therefore, for the storage of these finished products. In only the special-order type of manufacturing plant is this factor of minimum importance.

Furthermore, in order to carry on manufacturing

Purchase, Control and Storing Materials

operations economically, it is common practice in most plants to set up certain machines for producing ahead of time certain parts in large lots in order to reduce the cost of set-up per part. These parts are stored in what is known as the finished-parts storeroom, and drawn out again as they may be required for final assemblies.

16. *Ordering materials for production.* Requisitions for materials regularly carried in stores are drawn on the storeroom, and the storeskeeper places purchase requisitions with the purchase agent when the quantity on hand has fallen to a predetermined low stock or order point.

The ordering of materials for special work to be done to order, or for repair work, is usually done by the production planning department upon receipt of drawings, specifications and bills of materials on such work. A check is made with the storeroom first, however, since it is possible that something may be carried in stores which will fill the need. If the work is to extend over a considerable length of time, the rates or times of delivery of the materials are carefully planned by either the engineering or planning department, to prevent tying up money in materials in stores a long time in advance of need.

In continuous industries, and in those making standardized products in large quantities, storeskeeping becomes merely a problem of keeping in touch with the rates of production, and of establishing maximum and minimum limits on the amounts carried in stores. The purpose of the maximum limit is to prevent over-investment, while that of the minimum limit is to assure the replenishment of supplies before any interruption of production occurs.

17. *Methods of regulating stores and stocks.* Because storerooms and stock rooms are required to anticipate the needs of the shop and the market, they have to be organized to perform the following functions along the lines of accepted standard procedure:

- (a) Requisition from the purchasing department an economical amount of the proper materials for delivery at the most advantageous time.
- (b) Inspect all received materials as to quantity and quality.
- (c) Properly store and safeguard all materials.
- (d) Issue materials on properly authorized materials-issue orders.
- (e) Maintain adequate records as to receipts and expenditures.
- (f) Maintain balances of materials on hand sufficient to serve production needs, that is, continuous or running inventories.

Storage arrangement depends upon the character of the materials involved. The usual practice is to store materials so that they can be easily located and issued, as well as easily checked when a count is necessary.

Usually, each lot of material, or each bin or storage place, is numbered, or otherwise designated, so that the material can be found by referring to an index list. The mnemonic system, whereby use is made of symbolic letters which are sometimes amplified by numbers, finds wide application in storeroom and stock room operation. Various combinations of letters and numbers may be adopted. For example, the symbol 8B–29J may stand for Building Number 8, division B, section 29 and bin J.

18. *Maximum and minimum limits.* Factory materials usually fall into three classes: standard materials, special materials, and supplies. The demand for such materials changes from time to time, but the amounts on hand of each item are never allowed to fall below an established minimum, which may be changed from time to time according to variations in sales and production. When materials are ordered for the replenishment of stores, the order is for an amount that will not bring the total on hand above an established maximum limit.

Instead of using maximum and minimum limits, firms may have specified order points and standard ordering quantities. These are recorded on the balance-of-stores sheet for each item. When the available amount of a material falls to the established order point, a requisition is made out for the purchase or manufacture of the predetermined quantity of the material. This is sufficient to bring the total amount of the materials on hand up to the fixed maximum at the time the new supply is received.

19. *Continuous or perpetual inventories.* In most plants, stores and stock records are kept by a clerical staff working under the direction of an inventory control supervisor. These records consist of either a series of loose-leaf ledgers or a card system. The purpose of such inventory records is to show the exact amounts of materials on order, the quantities on hand, how much of the latter has been apportioned or reserved for orders going through, and how much is available for manufacturing operations that are not yet scheduled.

20. *Operating the finished-parts storeroom.* Standard machine parts, such as bolts and screws, if made in the plant instead of being purchased, are delivered to the storeroom just as though they had been obtained by purchase. Machine elements, such as gears, pulleys, bearings and coupling, which are to be stored and redrawn for final assembly into completed machines, present a somewhat different problem.

If the business is a large one, a separate storeroom, known as a finished-parts storeroom, may be maintained as previously stated. In most plants, however, one storeroom cares for both raw materials and finished parts. In any case, a careful and systematic record is kept of such parts, usually on the continuous inventory plan. The cost of the finished parts may or may not be entered on this record. To save rehandling the stores issue slips for pricing in the cost department, however, the usual procedure is to have the costs entered on the inventory records and put on the stores issue slips when

Purchase, Control and Storing Materials

the records are posted. The extensions of the figures for cost purposes are done later in the cost department of the company.

21. *Finished-stock record.* Just as it is necessary to have accurate records of raw materials and finished parts, so it is necessary to have accurate records of finished stock. Such records not only guide the manager in placing production orders, but, also, if properly studied, prevent the accumulation of obsolete stock. Records of this kind are usually kept on loose-leaf ledger sheets.

A sheet devoted to each item of stock shows all receipts from the factory, all shipments, and the balances on hand. The dates of all receipts and shipments are also recorded. This item is important for two reasons: first, to show the rate of shipment as a measure of required rate of production; and, second, to gage depreciation and obsolescence when inventory is taken. The obsolescence factor is highly important, especially in a business that is developing rapidly.

The stock records give the location of the items that they record, the order points and standard ordering quantities, and the values. The stores ledger, the active accounts in the cost ledger, and the stock ledger constitute a continuous inventory. From these records there can be obtained at any time the value of all materials grouped in the three important stages of fabrication, namely, as raw materials, as work-in-process, and as finished products.

22. *Physical inventories.* With stores ledgers, stock ledgers, and cost ledgers, which record the changes in value of the work-in-process, a complete perpetual inventory is maintained of all materials in the form of raw stores, work-in-process, and finished products. Occasionally, however, an actual physical inventory is made to verify these running inventories. This check-up is usually made by the storeskeeper, bin by bin, as a continuous process during his spare time, or on request of the balance-of-stores clerk for a check on certain items.

Review

Explain why the position held by a purchasing agent is an important one.

Name some of the means which a purchasing agent has at his disposal for saving his company money in buying materials.

Why should a purchasing agent have a working knowledge of commercial law?

What are the advantages of centralizing purchasing in a plant?

Give a brief summary of the duties of a purchasing agent.

In what departments of a plant do requisitions for materials originate?

What are some of the factors to take into consideration when preparing specifications for materials to be purchased?

Purchase, Control and Storing Materials

Differentiate between storerooms and stock rooms and explain the necessity for such storage places.

Describe the standard procedure followed by storerooms and stock rooms in performing their functions.

What is meant by maximum and minimum limits in connection with the storage of materials?

CHAPTER X

Inspection and Quality Control

1. *Control of quality.* Statistical quality control is a proved system for maintaining uniform standards of manufacturing quality at a minimum cost, and is a major contribution to manufacturing efficiency. It effects substantial savings in cost of production by preventing waste, eliminating rework, and reducing the duplication of inspection, and assures that a high uniform quality product will leave the manufacturing plant.

By providing a common measure of quality, it greatly facilitates understanding between producer and consumer, and helps to insure acceptance of a quality-controlled product. Altogether, statistical quality control is becoming recognized in industrial plants as the ultimate of efficient management. It has become standard operating procedure for acceptance-inspection programs.

Statistical quality control may appear difficult, but only because the mathematical principles upon which it is based are not immediately obvious. Once the common sense of these simple mathematical principles is appreciated, this new approach—a new way of thinking—for inspection, process control, test evaluation and

Inspection and Quality Control

management organization finds its widespread application.

2. *Piece-to-piece variation of parts.* In manufacturing, a "piece-to-piece variation" will exist among parts of an identical kind, maybe produced on the same equipment. At first glance, they may look alike; actually, they may differ slightly in every dimension. This fact may be quickly revealed by a few experimental measurements. Every piece varies in some degree from every other piece, but this variation, when controlled and kept within tolerances, does not cause trouble. Production men and inspectors are familiar with this variation between seemingly identical pieces. It occurs even under comparatively stable manufacturing conditions.

The piece-to-piece variation in press or machine-made products, as shown in Figure 10, follows a definite pattern which can be discovered by testing and sorting a sample lot. The amount of deviation from form is made evident by the use of regular inspection fixtures. In the case of assemblies, shape is sometimes one of the quality characteristics with which the manufacturer is concerned. The piece-to-piece variation of this quality characteristic may be shown by the difference in deviation of the individual pieces of a manufactured lot.

3. *Grouping according to piece-to-piece variations.* As pieces are checked, they are grouped according to the amount of deviation. Those with the least amount of deviation are placed in a group at one end. As the de-

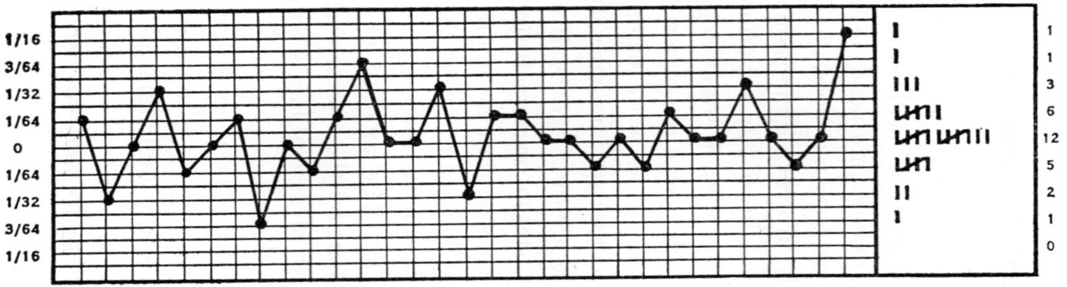

FIGURE 10—TYPICAL STATISTICAL QUALITY CONTROL CHART

Inspection and Quality Control

viation increases, others are placed at the extreme end. Inherently, more pieces will be stacked in the middle groups than in the groups at either end. A chart or graph of the variations, as to extent of dimensional variation and the number of pieces in each group, is shown in Figure 11.

This illustration is a tally of the number of pieces sorted by the operator into groups. The preceding discussion indicated that more items were placed in the middle groups—or class intervals—than in the groups or class intervals at the extremes. The illustration shows how many fell into each group or class interval. The resultant pattern or count of the items according to class interval is known as "frequency distribution." Frequency distribution furnishes a measure of the piece-to-piece variation of a product.

The chart shows at a glance the characteristic frequency distribution or pattern of variation that comes from measuring, sorting and counting 70 or so pieces out of a single lot of a machine-made product.

Figure 12 shows the pattern that would result from measuring, sorting, and counting a lot of 1,000 pieces. It is considerably smoother and more symmetrical than the distribution of a lot of 100. This tendency of the distribution to become more regular as more pieces are tested will continue indefinitely. When a very large number of samples is tested, the pattern approaches its true bell-shaped form.

It has been demonstrated many times in practical

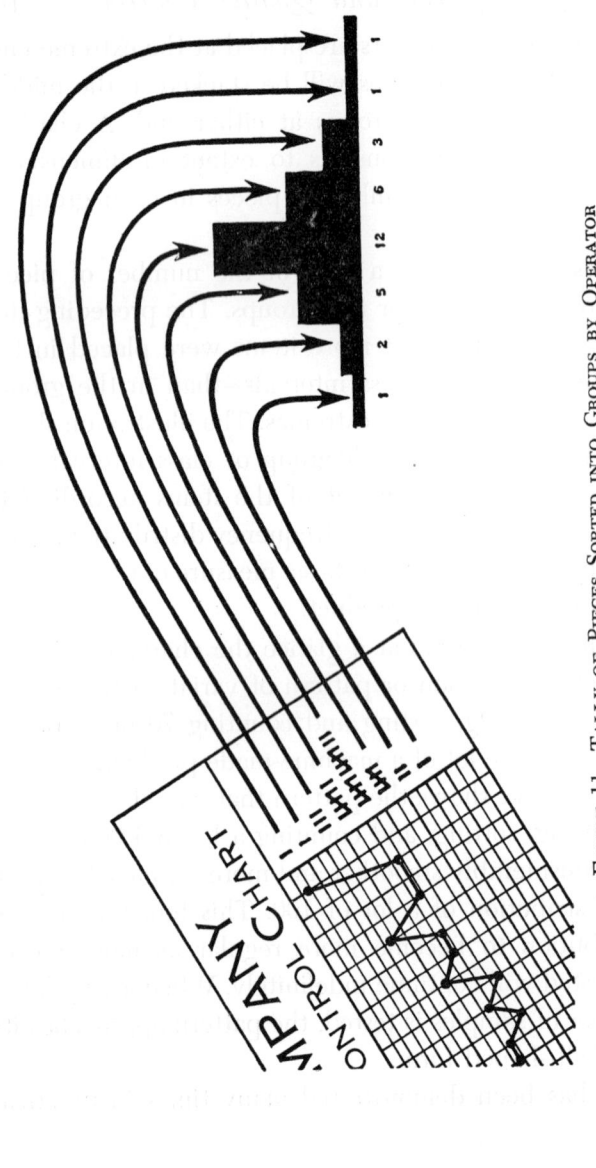

FIGURE 11—TALLY OF PIECES SORTED INTO GROUPS BY OPERATOR

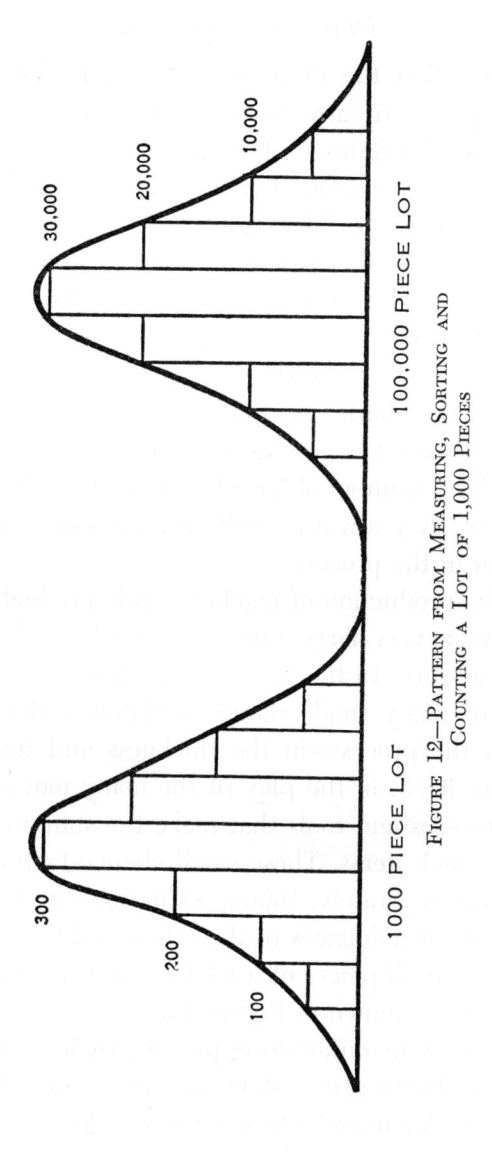

Figure 12—Pattern from Measuring, Sorting and Counting a Lot of 1,000 Pieces

experience that the measurement of very large numbers of pieces of any manufactured product always results in a definite and persistent pattern. Almost always the patterns closely approximate normal curves, but occasionally, and for ascertained reasons, they appear as skewed—that is, non-symmetrical—curves. But, whether skewed or normal, they follow the same general principles.

There is a cause for the similarity of patterns which occurs in the charts for different products, and mathematical theory has provided the answer. It shows that when a large number of "small chance causes" influence a process, they always result in a definite pattern of variation in the process.

In the production of machine-made products, there is always a very large number of such small chance causes at work. In the case of stampings, for example, there are many small chance variations all the way through the process—in the thickness and temper of the sheet itself, in the play of the many moving parts of the presses and tools that make the stampings, and in other such items. These small chance factors affect each piece separately. Influences in one direction tend to cancel out influences in the other, and the resultant variations in all pieces of a lot form a definite pattern, such as those shown in Figure 13.

For every manufacturing process, such a pattern of variation always exists. But, even more important, for any particular manufacturing process, its own pattern

Inspection and Quality Control

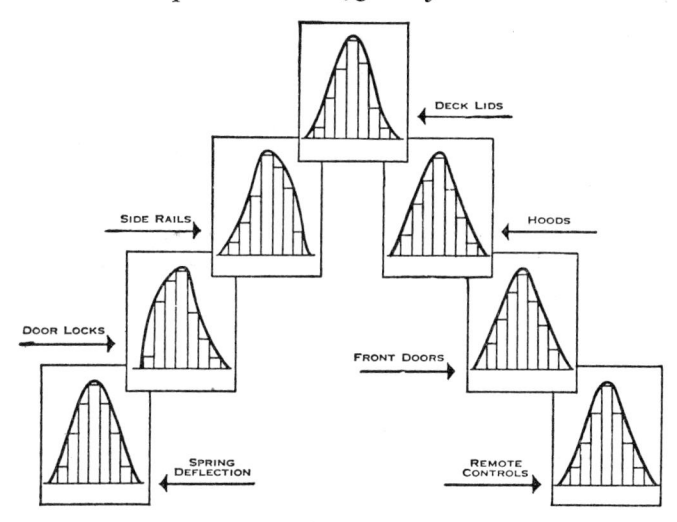

FIGURE 13—RESULTANT VARIATIONS IN ALL PIECES OF
A LOT FORM A DEFINITE PATTERN

will be repeated over and over again as long as the same chance causes are at work.

4. *Predicting the proper limits of a process.* From the fact that the pattern of variation in a manufacturing process repeats itself, comes the ability to predict the proper limits of the process in the future, in the absence of fundamental change. This is the scientific basis of statistical quality control. As long as the pattern remains unchanged, there is the assurance that there is no new or "assignable" cause of variation which has affected the production process. Without change in chance causes, the pattern repeats itself hourly, daily and monthly within predictable limits.

Good production comes when the pattern is repeated over and over again within the tolerance limits established for the item being produced. When the pattern is known to fall within tolerance limits, there is assurance that the entire production is acceptable, and there is no need for concern over the acceptability of each individual piece by itself. The process as a whole is said to be "in control" within tolerance limits.

5. *Departure from pattern.* Departure from the established pattern is a certain sign that something is wrong. The product is no longer being affected only by small chance factors. A basic change has occurred in the conditions affecting production, an assignable cause of variation that must be tracked down and eliminated.

Some basic changes in manufacturing conditions, such as tool (die) wear, may cause the frequency-distribution pattern to shift so that all, or part, of it is beyond one tolerance limit or the other. Other changes, such as material instability, cause greater piece-to-piece variation and a flattening out of the pattern, so that one or both of the extremes are beyond tolerance limits. In either case, quality suffers and scrap and waste result.

With statistical quality control, it is possible to spot such troubles almost instantly and bring the whole process back into control. Obviously, this could not be done if testing had to wait until the whole lot had been produced.

Figure 14 graphs in diagram form the pattern of

Inspection and Quality Control 171

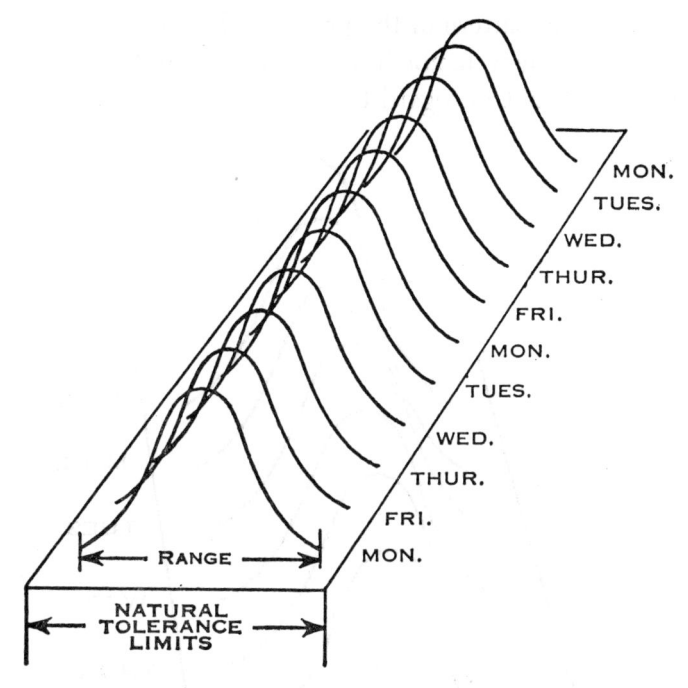

FIGURE 14—PATTERN OF NATURAL LIMITS FOR A PRODUCT
ACCORDING TO PREDICTIONS

natural limits for a product according to predictions. Figure 15 illustrates a distribution shift from the natural tolerance limits, and Figure 16 shows an instance of increased variation, where the spread has been widened in both directions.

6. *Lot sampling.* The methods of statistical quality control require only the periodic measurement of a small sample, often only five to ten pieces, so as to detect any trouble in manufacturing. The sample will

show if the pattern of the process is being maintained, or if some new factor has suddenly disrupted it. The concern is not in regard to sample pieces as such, but

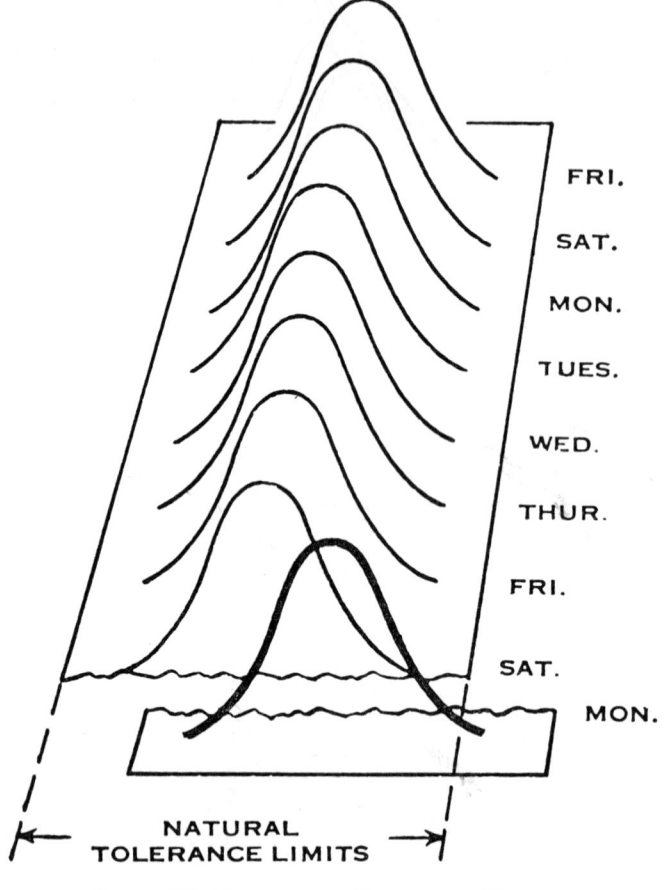

FIGURE 15—DISTRIBUTION SHIFT FROM NATURAL TOLERANCE LIMITS

Inspection and Quality Control 173

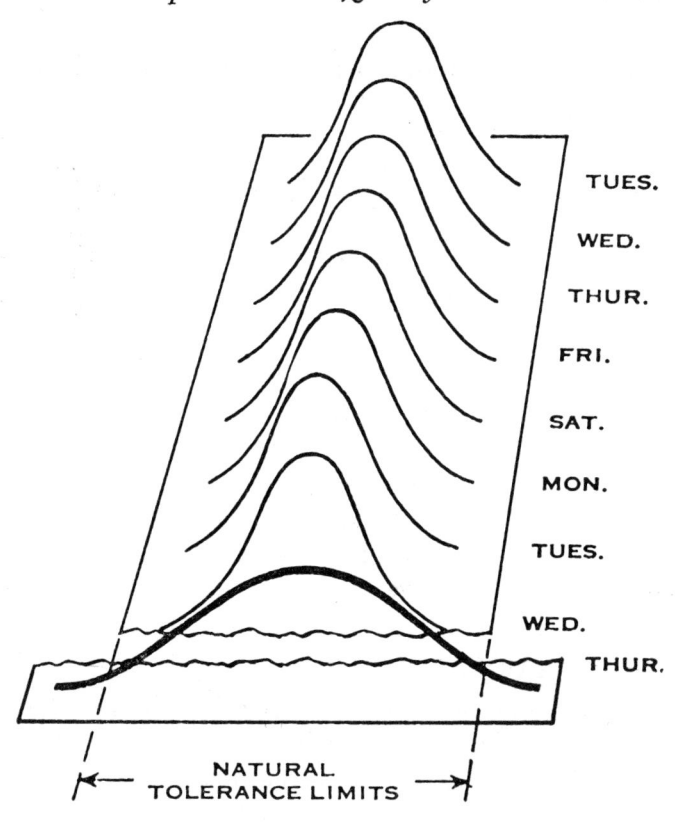

FIGURE 16—INCREASED VARIATION-SPREAD WIDENED
IN BOTH DIRECTIONS

instead the information which they give on the entire lot.

The sample is selected at random for testing. Thus, the individual units in the sample are assembled without regard as to which portion of the lot they were in.

In this manner, the sample reflects the characteristics of the group within limits that can be predicted with mathematical accuracy. There are always chance risks in sampling, but such risks can be held to whatever limits are best for the balancing of the factors of accuracy and economy.

The individual pieces in a group of parts will practically all fall within the limits of the group as shown by its frequency distribution or normal curve. Units of a sample drawn from a production lot will therefore fall within these same limits.

The average of such a sample will fall within certain narrower limits—the highs tending to cancel the lows—which are calculated from the natural tolerance limits by a simple formula. These limits of the sample average are usually designated as "control limits," the lower control limit being designated LCL and the upper limit UCL.

If a sample average falls outside of these control limits, it is almost certain that the sample does not come from the original lot of the production material. This occurrence is a signal that an assignable cause—in addition to the usual small chance causes—has entered into the process and caused the production lot to shift, or become more variable. Figure 17 illustrates this point.

7. *The control chart.* The control chart furnishes a convenient and efficient means for continuous checking to see whether the pattern of the process is repeating

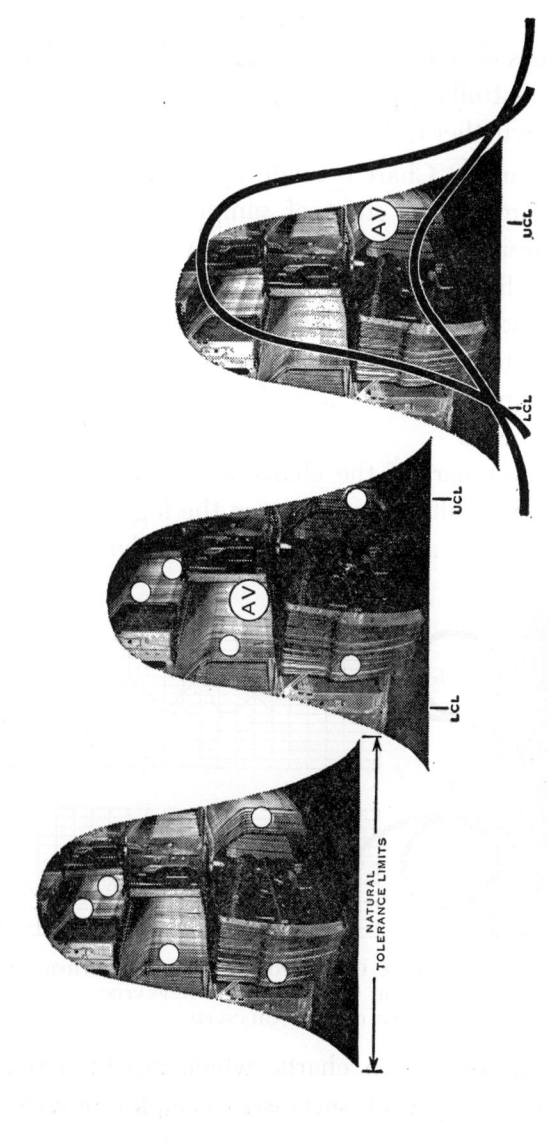

FIGURE 17—Sample Average Falling Outside of the Control Limits

176 *Plant Management*

itself, or has changed. The "P" Chart is used for checking and controlling process averages, and is used to designate whether each unit is good or bad.

The $\overline{X}$ and $\overline{R}$ Chart is made up of two parts. The top part provides a chart of sample averages taken from an operation every hour. If the averages keep falling within limits UCL and LCL, the pattern has not changed and is reproducing itself through periods of time. The product from this process is held in control—it is uniform within the normal variations of the production process.

The lower part of the chart shows sample ranges, measuring the differences between the highest and the lowest value in each sample. Figure 18 shows the re-

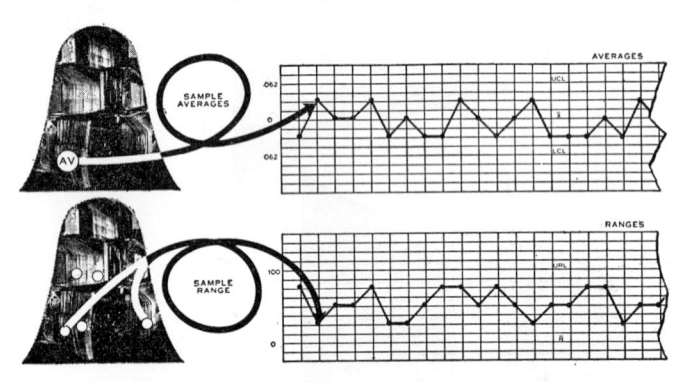

FIGURE 18—CONTROL CHART FOR CHECKING WHETHER THE PATTERN OF THE PROCESS IS REPEATING ITSELF OR HAS CHANGED

cordings on these two charts, which are plotted together. The ranges of successive samples provide a

Inspection and Quality Control

measure of process variation and should fall within the limits of O to URL in the chart of Figure 19.

8. *Use of the control chart.* The control chart will point out departures from established patterns. A shift

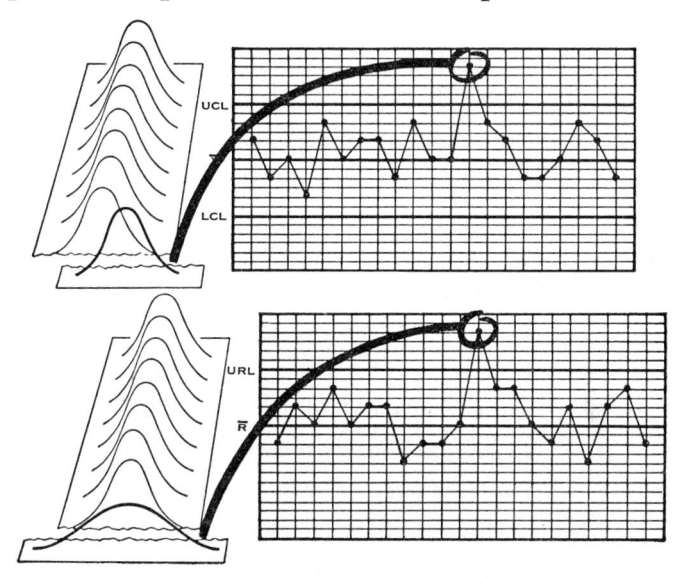

FIGURE 19—RANGES OF SUCCESSIVE SAMPLES PROVIDING A MEASURE OF PROCESS VARIATIONS

in the process will be indicated by a sample average appearing outside of the control limits. A flattening of the distribution because of operator carelessness, or wear in the machine, will be indicated by a sample above the upper range limit. In this way, the charts give certain and immediate information about patterns of variation in the process. They can be used where actual measurements are made on each piece in the sample (variables) or when each unit is classed only as good or bad (attributes).

Materials that come into the plant with variations from standard sizes can be separated and progressively graded to be fed into presses so as to have machine-setting changes made in only one direction, thus saving much time. Through use of the control chart and the making of die adjustments, materials can be kept within limits of requirements. The quality of entire runs of materials may be controlled by the inspection of small samples—sufficient to provide the necessary check—and the use of statistical quality control methods.

Review

What is meant by "statistical quality control"?

How does statistical quality control reduce costs?

To what does the term "piece-to-piece variation" refer?

What is a characteristic of piece-to-piece variation?

Define "frequency distribution" and describe a method of how it is determined.

What is meant by "small chance variations"?

What is the scientific basis of statistical quality control?

How does statistical quality control make it possible to spot troubles arising from basic changes in the conditions affecting production?

Describe the control chart and state its purpose.

CHAPTER XI

Plant Buildings, Machinery and Layout

1. *Selection of a suitable factory.* In selecting a suitable type of factory building, the important factor to be taken into consideration is the nature of the manufacturing process that will be carried on in the building. In highly-specialized industries, such as chemical plants and ore-reducing mills, or in plants engaged in mass production of assembled products, the manufacturing processes require special types of buildings. In many lines of manufacturing, however, buildings of a general type, well constructed and designed, are suitable.

If a building constructed to meet general requirements can be used, such a building is preferable to one that is merely adapted to the housing of some specialized process. One reason for this is that technical developments may make it necessary for the company to change to some other process before the building has been in use for any great length of time. Buildings suitable for general requirements offer much greater flexibility in meeting such changes. Furthermore, such buildings are likely to bring a better price if a company later decides to sell its plant.

2. *Methods of planning and engineering.* In plant construction and factory layout, buildings and equipment must conform to the requirements of the management and workers who use them. Hence, factory planning calls for a correct balance among the human, financial, production and engineering factors in manufacturing. Four principal methods may be employed for accomplishing this. These are as follows:

   (a) Engaging the services of a local architect or local engineer.
   (b) Placing of the entire responsibility on one of the large industrial engineering firms that has specialized in the planning of new plants.
   (c) Employment of a competent engineer on a full-time salary to supervise the planning and construction of the new plant.
   (d) Engaging the services of a firm of contracting engineers and builders which will assume the responsibility of planning and constructing the buildings required.

No matter which method is adopted, the factory engineering staff itself should be available for constant consultation and advice.

3. *The use of process flow charts.* The layout of a plant should be such as to allow the materials being processed to flow through it in the shortest time and at minimum cost. In a plant making a single product, this is readily accomplished by placing the various departments in proper sequence of operation. In a multi-

Plant Buildings, Machinery and Layout 181

product plant, however, where numerous products are continually passing through the departments, the layout is more complex.

To aid in visualizing the flow of work through man-

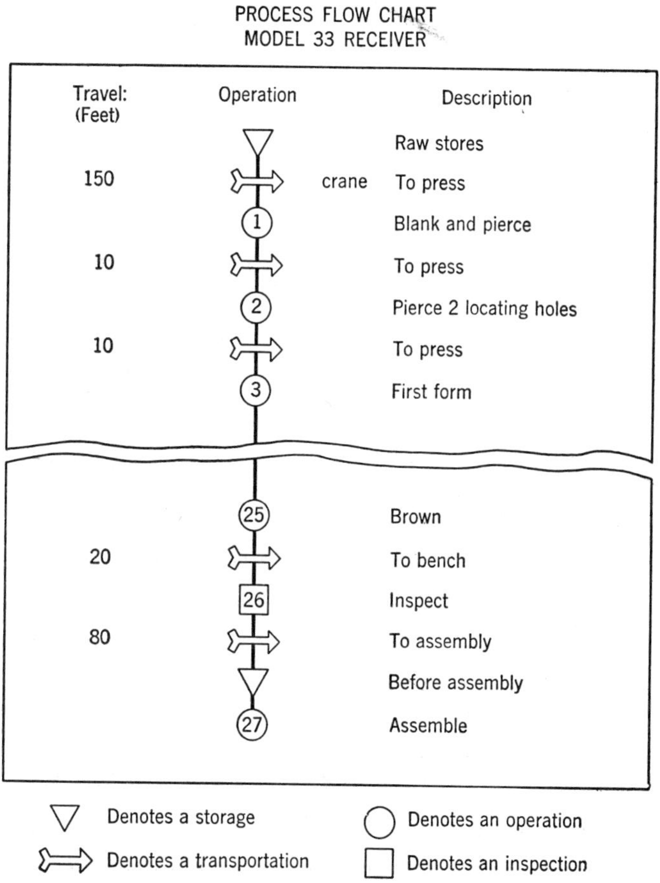

PROCESS FLOW CHART
MODEL 33 RECEIVER

Travel: (Feet)	Operation		Description
	▽		Raw stores
150	⇨	crane	To press
	①		Blank and pierce
10	⇨		To press
	②		Pierce 2 locating holes
10	⇨		To press
	③		First form
	㉕		Brown
20	⇨		To bench
	▢ 26		Inspect
80	⇨		To assembly
	▽		Before assembly
	㉗		Assemble

▽ Denotes a storage ◯ Denotes an operation
⇨ Denotes a transportation ▢ Denotes an inspection

FIGURE 20—PROCESS FLOW CHART

ufacturing plants, engineers have devised two most useful tools. These are the process flow chart and the flow diagram. The process flow chart shows a chart form, by use of symbols and brief descriptions, the storages, operations, transportations, and inspections pertaining to a given part or material passing through a factory. Such a chart is shown in Figure 20.

The process flow chart is valuable not only in enabling the layout engineer to visualize what may take place in a new plant, but also in analyzing an existing layout with a view to making improvements.

4. *Flow diagrams.* A flow diagram differs from a process flow chart in that the flow of work is shown on a floor plan of the factory. It is the final step in factory planning before the actual arrangement of machinery and equipment begins. Figure 21 is an illustration of a typical flow diagram.

5. *Fundamental factors in plant layout.* Provided no land-area limitations are imposed, machines and equipment should be arranged so as to provide for the best manufacturing sequences, without reference to the building lines. In other words, if general-purpose buildings are inadequate, the factory layout should be planned first, and the buildings built around them.

Where industrial buildings are so designed that they fit the processes carried on within them, they form an integral part of the production cycle. Such plants may be looked upon as in themselves big machines containing and coordinating all the little machines.

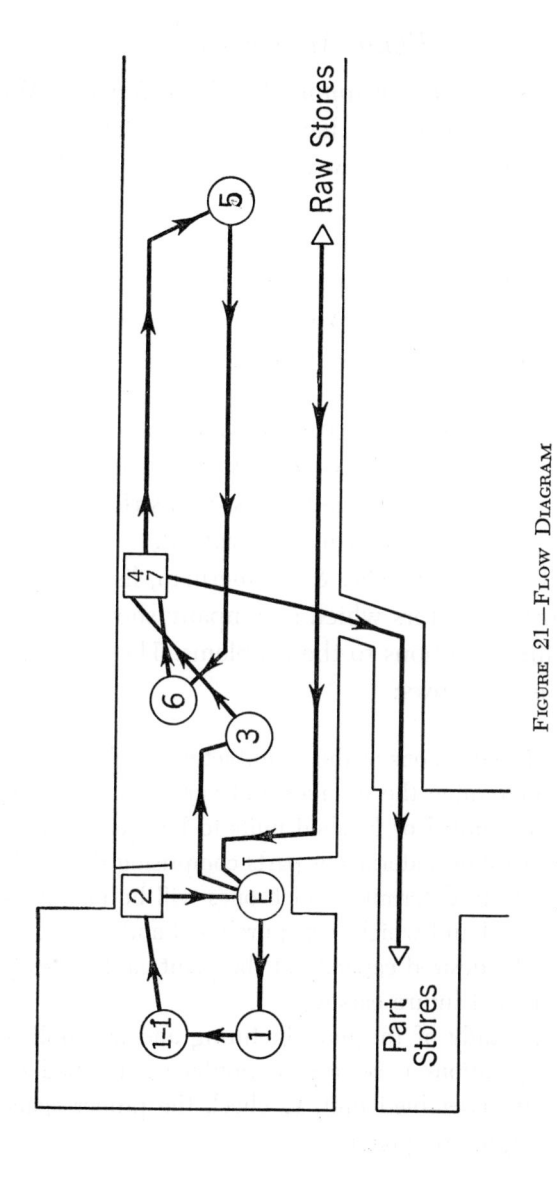

FIGURE 21—Flow Diagram

6. *Procedures in developing the basic layout.* When detailed flow diagrams have been completed and coordinated into a final flow diagram for the whole plant, the next step is to ascertain the amount of machine equipment that is necessary for the various processes. The selection of equipment may be a question of relative simplicity, or one involving great detail and study. If the plant is a simple, continuous-process industry, such as a salt plant, ore-reducing plant, or cement works, the problems of factory layout and equipment selection are comparatively easy to solve. In all but such simple, continuous-process industries, however, the problems are much more involved.

H. T. Moore, of Day & Zimmerman, lists a number of important factors which a company should consider in reaching solutions to the problems. The list of these factors is as follows:

(a) The divisions of the manufacturing schedule, to determine the number and variety of the sub-assembled or finished units to be produced.
(b) A list of materials or parts comprising the product, to determine which ones will be manufactured and which ones purchased and stored.
(c) The desired capacity of the plant, and the estimated future capacity.
(d) A study of the manufacturing and assembling operations necessary to produce a finished or sub-assembled unit, to check the proper spacing of equipment.

Plant Buildings, Machinery and Layout

(e) The sequence of operations in manufacturing and assembly departments in order that departments and equipments shall be in logical and convenient relationship for the progressive flow of materials.

(f) The production equipment or plant facilities needed for the desired capacity of the initial plant, including any special provisions or structural features that will facilitate production.

(g) The time interval required between successive operations, if any, to check the need for, and location of, storage space.

(h) A review of the various operations entering into the process, to determine whether certain departments should be isolated from the standpoint of safety, noise or special process needs.

(i) The space requirements per department to house the production equipment and provide space for aisles, storage or auxiliary departments.

(j) A summary of the floor space needs of the initial plant, to determine which areas can be proportionately increased for the different departments, based on an assumed future capacity after a certain period of years, thus providing an approximate basis for estimating the space requirements and development of a suitable layout for the ultimate plant development.

(k) Consultation with other departments to check the layout from the standpoint of methods engineering, materials handling, and other fundamentals affecting operation.

7. *Analysis of product.* The engineering and planning departments furnish analyses of the detailed designs and manufacturing methods to be carried out in processing the product. The times required to perform the various operations are supplied by the time-study department, while the paths or routes to be followed are worked out in the planning department. From such analyses, compilations may be made as to the number of machines and other devices and equipment needed.

8. *Selection of equipment.* When the number of machines and other equipment of each type required is known, selection of the particular kind to install is the next step. A committee made up of company executives and engineers may make the selection, in consultation with equipment engineers familiar with the machinery in the particular field of manufacturing. Manufacturers of high-grade machines and equipment are always willing to cooperate in making detailed studies and layouts of processes in which their clients may be interested.

9. *Fundamental methods of machine arrangement.* There are two fundamental methods of machine arrangement in manufacturing plants. One method is to group together all machines of a similar kind, such as planers, milling machines, or lathes, in a department or a separate area. All work to be done on any machine of the particular kind must be sent to that particular area. There is no definite arrangement of the different departments in relation to one another. This method is known as "process layout," and a good example is the

Plant Buildings, Machinery and Layout

ordinary job shop. Manufacturing is usually intermittent according to special orders.

The other method exists typically in plants making specific products on a mass production basis. Here, the equipment is arranged according to the sequence of operations performed on specific parts, subassemblies and assemblies. Flow of work is direct through all operations from start to finish on a particular product. If a plant makes more than one product on a large scale, each product has its own equipment and layout known as a "product layout." Typical illustrations are the continuous type industries, such as foundries, steel plants, and chemical plants, and the repetitive mass production industries, such as the automotive, clothing, typewriter and washing machine plants.

10. *Process layout.* Where the product is not and cannot be standardized, or where the volume of like work is low, a layout according to the operations or processes performed is practically required. Such a condition requires flexibility in manufacturing sequence which is readily obtainable with this method of layout.

Furthermore, with all like machines grouped in one department, workers and supervisors become highly skilled in their operation, thus producing better quality work at lower cost, and, with all machines alike, the employee training for a given department is easier. Investment in machines and equipment may be less, since it is not necessary to have a complete set of machines for every product produced. By proper scheduling of operations on different products, one machine may be sufficient where two or more would be required under a product layout. If this is the case, that machine will be active a large share of the time, an advantageous situation from the cost standpoint.

With process layout, however, the amount of handling is large, thus increasing the manufacturing time and the quantity of handling equipment, both of which add to cost. Moreover, the control of production—scheduling and dispatching to bring the work to the right department at the right time—is complicated and the chance of delay in delivery is increased. Also, the paper work of production control is considerable and greatly detailed. Inspections, often required before a product leaves one department for the next, delay production and add to cost. Cost of investment of work-in-process is usually high, because of the amount and longer time in trucking and the consequent increase in parts waiting to be processed.

Figure 22 is a graphical representation of the fundamental principles involved in process layouts. Manufacturing is departmentalized according to the processes employed in production, the layout segregating all like machines or processes in a department by themselves.

11. *Product layout.* The product method of layout is also known as the straight-line or direct method. As the name implies, there is a concentration of attention upon the characteristics of the product to be produced

Courtesy Professor K. C. White

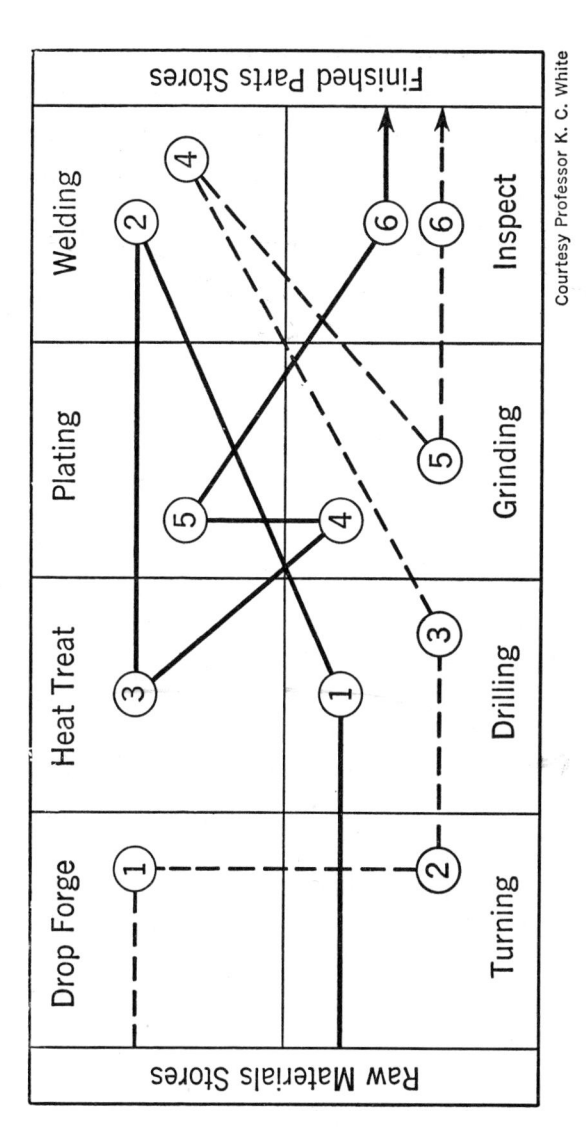

––––– Product A   ——— Product B

FIGURE 22—FLOW OF WORK UNDER A TYPICAL PROCESS LAYOUT OF DEPARTMENTS

and, accordingly, machines are arranged with this purpose in view. Thus, a department making turret lathes has its own equipment, especially adapted to its needs. Another department building automatic lathes has its own special equipment. Each department is entirely independent of the other and, in a large measure, self-sufficient in so far as machine processes are concerned.

If such complete specialization of product is not desirable, the factory may be so planned as to complete certain major parts or unit assemblies of parts, with the individual piece or pieces remaining in a single department until they are ready for final assembly. By this method, a manufacturing plant becomes a series of small factories, enabling its administrators to capitalize the advantages accruing from straight-line flow of production, visual executive production control, simplified cost accounting, and other factors of efficiency.

For product layout, a well-standardized product and the output of large quantities of this product are generally necessary. In some instances, a line of machines may be set up to produce a given order of a few parts and then rearranged for the requirements of the next order. In general, however, product layout is best adapted to the mass production industries. The automotive industry is an outstanding example of what may be done in production by straight-lining. Nevertheless, the principles of straight-lining can be, and have been, applied in many other industries.

In product layout of machines, all emphasis is

Plant Buildings, Machinery and Layout

placed on the product. The machines required in the processing of the product are brought together in one department and set up in accordance with the chosen sequence of operations. For example, in the machining of the case for an automobile transmission, all of the machines required are located in one department. The rough castings for the passenger car transmission case enter the line of operation at one end, and leave at the other end as a completely machined and assembled case ready for the final car assembly line.

Since such a line of equipment is set up for a certain required production per hour, and the machine for each operation is selected with that output in mind, the product will flow along smoothly with little delay. Idle machine time will occur, however, where the potential production of a machine is greater than that required of the line as a whole. Line production of this kind may also necessitate duplication of equipment which might be avoided with a process layout where the machine, after finishing its work on one product, could be used for another product.

When the product is completely manufactured in one department, a visual check can be made of the progress or stoppages, thus improving coordination of work and simplifying production-control procedures, paper work, inspections, and the like. Production control, however, becomes more vital because if anything holds up the delivery of raw material to the line, the whole line is shut down. Consequently, it cannot be used readily to produce other items during the delay. Provision must also be made for the immediate repair or replacement of machines in line production to prevent a breakdown from holding up the entire line.

A graphical representation of the product method of layout is shown in Figure 23. Manufacturing is departmentalized according to the products produced, the layout of machines being in accord with the successive processes required, so that the product moves largely in a "straight line" through the factory.

12. *Drawing board layouts.* Having considered all the factors in the particular layout to be adopted, and having decided on the quantity and types of each class of equipment required, the engineering staff is ready to proceed with the actual layout work. This method of procedure is to plan carefully the arrangement of departments on layout boards, photostat these layouts, and send copies for approval to those higher in authority. Inspection and criticism of layouts by the higher executives is of greatest importance, because they are responsible for the ultimate success or failure in the operation of the factory.

The most widely used method of planning layouts is known as the "template method." The over-all shapes of the various units of equipment are drawn to scale on stiff paper and are then cut out along the outlines. These small diagrams or templates are then arranged in logical relative positions on the drawings of the floor plans of the departments in which the machines are

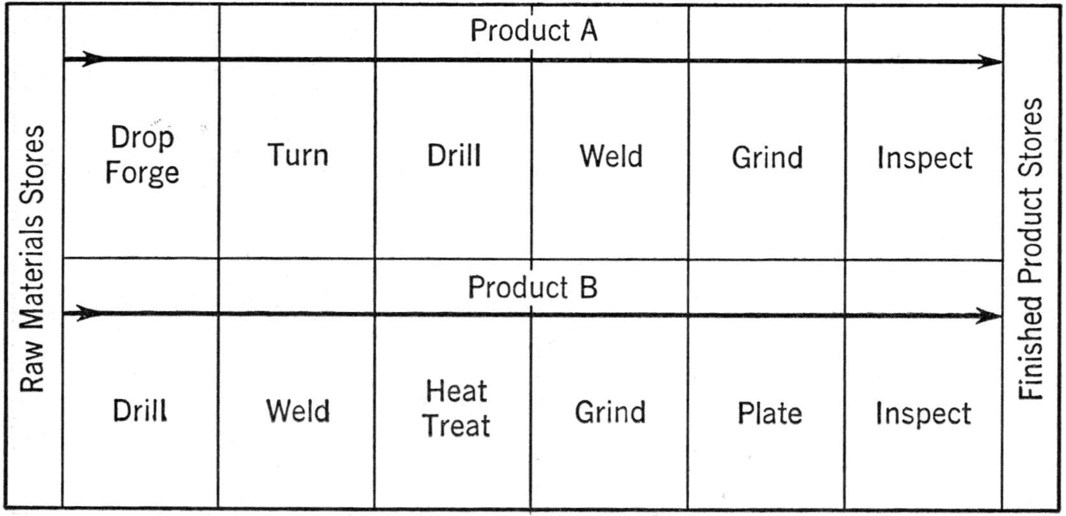

Raw Materials Stores					
Drop Forge	Turn	Drill	Weld	Grind	Inspect
		Product A →			
Drill	Weld	Heat Treat	Grind	Plate	Inspect
		Product B →			
Finished Product Stores					

Courtesy Professor K. C. White, Cornell University

FIGURE 23—FLOW OF WORK UNDER A TYPICAL PRODUCT OR STRAIGHT-LINE LAYOUT

to be placed, as dictated by the operation sheets and flow diagrams. Usually, several possible solutions are worked out and submitted to each department for criticism, with the result that a final plan, incorporating the best from each layout, is developed, and sent to the higher administrative officers for approval.

An extension of the template idea is the use of three-dimensional scale models of machines and equipment. Where these are arranged in proper sequence, they give a correctly proportioned picture of the layout in miniature. By taking photographs of such layouts showing different possible arrangements, a ready means is afforded for comparing the respective set-ups and deciding which is the best and most economical for operation.

13. *Machine breakdowns and repairs.* Under the process layout, a machine breakdown does not result in a general plant stoppage. Furthermore, when there is a machine breakdown, urgent operations can be shifted readily to some similar machine. In the case of the product layout, however, a single machine breakdown will stop the entire line. Two types of provisions are taken to minimize such a plant tie-up: (1) immediate replacement of the crippled machine; and (2) providing a bank of work ahead of each operator.

The first expedient requires additional capital investment in machines; the second requires additional investment in work-in-process. The automobile industry, for the most part, replaces the crippled machine, or

Plant Buildings, Machinery and Layout 195

sets up a temporary machine through which it shunts the parts while the machine in the line is being repaired. In deciding which method to use, the cost factors of the one must be measured against those of the other. If a work bank is to be used, it must be large enough to keep each operator busy for the length of time taken to make the average repair. If the machine is to be replaced, or a temporary machine set up, aisle space and often crane service must be available.

Maintenance and machine repairs are factors to consider when positioning a machine. Arrangements must be made so as to have lubrication, adjustment and repair facilities readily accessible, or easy means must be provided for removing the machine for repairs, and for putting it back into position.

14. *Heating and ventilating.* Correct heating and ventilating contribute greatly to the comfort and well-being of employees, and the results are reflected in higher production and lower costs. Heating and ventilation engineers should be consulted on the design and selection of the system, which must be carefully coordinated with the layout and construction of the buildings.

Heating installations are usually classified as: (a) hot-air systems, (b) hot-water heat, (c) steam heating, or (d) electric heating, according to the heating medium used. These are further classified as direct radiation, indirect radiation, or combination system.

In many of the modern single-story, saw-tooth roof

buildings, the unit-heater system is used. Large steam coils enclosed in steel casing are placed at intervals throughout the shop, often in the roof trusses, and, by means of motor-driven fans, the heated air is circulated throughout the departments.

Ventilating systems may be either natural or mechanical, depending on the requirements of the product, the personnel employed, and the type of construction adopted. The heating and ventilating systems should be so operated that ideal atmospheric conditions are approached, namely 67 to 70 degrees Fahrenheit temperature, and a relative humidity of from 50 to 60 per cent.

15. *Air conditioning.* Air conditioning is the science of maintaining the atmosphere of an enclosure at any required temperature, humidity, and purity. In the broad sense, air conditioning includes heating and ventilating, as well as cooling, humidifying, and cleaning of air. A complete air-conditioning system does all simultaneously, heats or cools as the case may require, and attains and maintains other specified conditions.

From an industrial standpoint, complete air conditioning offers the following advantages:

- (a) Lower manufacturing costs by removing conditions which hamper manufacturing, such as atmospheric moisture and static electricity.
- (b) Improved quality of product as in the manufacture of chocolates.
- (c) Protection of goods in storage.

(d) Improved health of employees.

(e) Improved comfort and efficiency of employees.

16. *Factory illumination.* The ease of seeing without eye strain or tiring is fundamental to safe, efficient, economical operation in every industry. Good illumination is made up of more than simply a proper quantity of illumination. The proper quality—which includes the color of light, its direction, diffusion, steadiness, and absence of glare—is also important. Adequate illumination is a complex problem and, hence, installation of lighting facilities should be entrusted only to competent illumination engineers.

17. *Fire protection.* It is important that, in erecting a factory, provision is made for an adequate sprinkler system. The factory and its equipment will thus be protected and the fire insurance rates will be reduced. In addition to sprinklers, other means of protecting the factory against fire should be installed. These include water buckets, chemical extinguishers, hose wagons, yard hydrants, water tanks and fire pumps. It is also of great importance that requirements of state laws be met in connection with layouts of exits, their location relative to the workers, and other factors designed to reduce risks.

Review

Why should a manufacturing concern select a factory suitable for general requirements if it is possible for the company to use such a building?

What four methods may be employed in planning and constructing factory buildings?

Name some of the factors to consider in developing the basic layout of a plant.

What are the two fundamental methods of machine arrangement in manufacturing plants?

Describe the layout required where the product is not standardized and cannot be standardized.

Describe the layout which is best adapted for mass production industries.

What is the "template method" in planning factory layouts?

How can plant tie-ups because of machine breakdowns be minimized in plants having product layouts?

Name some of the advantages of air conditioning in factories.

What measures should be taken to provide fire protection?

CHAPTER XII

Materials Handling

1. *The high cost of handling materials.* It has been calculated that, on the average, from 22 per cent to as much as 35 per cent of today's dollar of manufacturing cost goes for the moving of materials into the industrial plant, through production, thence to the stock room or warehouse, and finally to the shipping platform and onto the transportation carrier. The cost is high when a great deal of hand labor is used for the purpose, and much lower when up-to-date handling equipment is used to move materials through the cycle of receiving, production and shipping.

It is possible that a suitable, well-devised installation of materials-handling equipment to replace inefficient methods will return the investment within as short a period as one year, or even less.

2. *Axioms of materials handling.* Materials handling adds not a cent to the basic value of the items moved. It merely—according to the reasoning of the economist —gives the materials "place utility." In view of this fact, all handling done should be subjected to frequent restudy. To guide in such studies, certain axioms or rules of materials handling have been assembled here:

(a) Handling should be reduced to a minimum by good layout.
(b) Distances over which materials are handled should be the shortest possible.
(c) Routes of materials should be on the same general level to the greatest extent that layout permits to avoid lifting and lowering.
(d) Once started in motion, materials should be kept moving constantly except when under actual operation, and even then when possible, as on moving assembly lines.
(e) Mechanical means should be used for handling materials wherever routes of travel and volume of work handled can be made to justify the investment in equipment. Hand handling is the most costly method to employ except for small volume of work.
(f) All materials-handling planning, engineering and supervision should be centralized under a central engineering and operating head or department. In a small plant, the duties would not take the full time of even one man, but they should nevertheless invariably be centralized.
(g) Materials-handling equipment should be standardized. A variety of equipment is usually necessary, each kind the best suited and most economical for its own purpose. Once a type is selected and found to be the best, however, it should be used also for all other similar handling work, to cut down repair-parts stores and simplify maintenance work.

Materials Handling

(h) Old equipment should be scrapped for new, if feasible, as soon as better equipment for lower-cost operation comes on the market. Magazines announcing new developments, and advertising literature sent in, should be regularly checked to get hold of better equipment.

(i) Materials-handling equipment is often interchangeable and advantage should be taken of this possibility. When occasion arises, it should be tried in places and for purposes other than those originally planned.

(j) The dollar spent for new materials-handling equipment often saves more than the dollar spent for new production equipment.

3. *Economies of efficient materials handling.* There are two major factors in materials handling, (a) the methods, and (b) the equipment. Sometimes, a change in methods of handling brings about considerable savings. In the main, however, equipment is the more important factor. Large savings result when equipment is adopted as a substitute for hand labor, or even when existing equipment is replaced by an improved or a more suitable type of equipment to do work. Few are the plants which are unable to use some kind of handling equipment to a distinct advantage.

In some cases, materials-handling equipment is installed not only to make the moving of materials easier, but to lift and transport loads that are far beyond human capacity to move without mechanical assistance.

The moving of the heavy ingots and billets in a steel mill, for example, and the loading and unloading of carloads of bulk materials, such as coal, sand, ore and pig iron, are jobs which cannot be satisfactorily handled by manpower with tongs or shovels, if at all.

In the large percentage of cases, however, the main and often the sole reason for using materials-handling equipment is that such equipment makes possible large savings in the cost of production. The economies obtained may be summed up as follows:

(a) Time and labor saved in unloading railroad cars, motor trucks, steamships, barges, and lighters, which deliver materials to plants.

(b) Elimination of considerable storeroom space and reduction of turnover time and overhead charges on inventories by moving incoming materials directly into production.

(c) Huge reductions in the cost of actually moving materials through production operations, by the use of various mechanical means.

(d) Higher production rates through keeping materials practically always on the move during processing, thus making greater use of plant manufacturing facilities.

(e) Elimination of costly hand-handling operations by substitution of:
    (1) Mechanical positioning of materials such as various small parts and fasteners, and feeding them to processing or assembly operations.

Materials Handling

- (2) Mechanical proportioning of materials on conveyor lines for supplying certain mixing or blending operations.
- (3) Mechanical moving of materials between processing stations on production lines.
- (4) Mechanical feeder machines for liquid or bulk products, such as sugar, flour, or cereals, located above conveyor lines for automatic filling or packaging, closing, labeling, cartoning and sealing of these products, as well as delivering the cartons directly to stock room or outgoing carriers.
- (5) Mechanical delivery of manufactured products or parts, from the end of production lines, over conveyor systems that carry them through packing operations to stock room, warehouse, or preferably directly onto outgoing carriers.

(f) Savings in manpower, and reduction of manufacturing delays and banks of work-in-process, by the tying together of consecutive series of operations on various floors of multistory buildings, thus also doing away with trucking and elevator service.

(g) Savings in electrical or mechanical power by use of the force of gravity to carry materials down chutes, inclined conveyors or ducts from upper floors.

4. *Methods of handling.* The receiving and shipping departments in a plant should be adjacent to sidings

or roadways or both, for convenience in unloading and loading railroad cars or motor trucks. In heavy-product industries, tracks and roadways are usually run directly into the manufacturing building.

Where the factory floor is at ground level, a common practice is to lower road or track level at the receiving point to bring the tailboard of the truck, or the floor of the freight car, level with the building floor. In many cases, the factory floor is up at the truck or car floor level.

For long internal hauls of heavy products between buildings in the yards of larger companies, railroad cars or motor trucks may be used. For shorter hauls to and from stock rooms, and between manufacturing operations, the use of the gasoline or electric motorized lift-platform trucks or fork trucks is common. Many of these are of the high-lift type.

The lift-platform trucks handle skids, while the fork trucks usually handle pallets. The latter, however, are often used to transport skids, or such items as barrels and drums. While this can be done with the bare forks, some fork trucks are equipped with interchangeable rams, up-enders, grabs and many other attachments which enable them to handle a wide range of products.

Local materials handling is often done by means of hand trucks. Many of these are of the ordinary two-wheel or four-wheel type. Wherever possible, however, hand trucks of the lifting type and also of the elevating or stacking type are used. They are mostly of the fork

Materials Handling

variety. Many of these are pulled by the operator, but the most useful types are those which are motor-driven. The latter have controls in the handle, so that the operator does no pulling, but merely guides the truck in transit.

Trailers, pallets, skids and tote boxes, which are used in connection with trucks, furnish convenient temporary storage devices where such are desired.

If trucks are widely used in multistory buildings, ramps to connect one floor with another are often provided to prevent sole dependence, or even any dependence, upon freight elevators with their attendant delays. Elevators, however, are usually indispensable, being used as materials-handling devices in most multistory buildings, especially for heavy articles.

Fork-truck handling is efficient up to 150 to 200 feet on repetitive work. At greater distances, tractor and trailer equipment is more economical, up to about 600 to 800 feet, or more.

Where a fixed route for the flow of materials can be established, and where the flow of materials is continuous, a power-driven belt conveyor, roller conveyor, or overhead monorail conveyor may be used economically for short or long distances. Liquids can be moved in pipes by gravity or pressure. Light powdered or flocculent materials can be moved through pipes or ducts which are pneumatically under pressure or suction. It should be noted, however, that when a change in the model produced requires a relayout of the plant, the change may have to conform somewhat to the location of these fixed conveyors systems, if the cost of moving them is high.

Short distance movement of materials from operation to operation may be accomplished by roller conveyors or chutes placed at a sufficient incline to cause the materials to be moved by gravity. In a multistory building, where subsequent departments can be placed one below the other, this is one of the cheapest methods of moving materials. Spiral gravity conveyors are often used where the transfer is practically vertical.

For single flow movement by gravity from machine to machine, the operations should not be so far apart as to require unnecessary stooping by the operator in picking up the parts or materials, especially if the product is heavy.

5. *Industrial-truck handling.* The wide variety of materials-handling equipment available precludes discussion here of the operation of all but one type of equipment which is very extensively used, namely, the lift truck. This was developed first as a platform truck for skid handling and later as a fork truck for pallet handling. It is a mobile unit, coming in capacities of from 1,000 pounds up to 20,000 pounds or more. It is applicable for handling materials inside or outside over fair roadways, and can be used in a wide range of work in plants, warehouses, and transportation.

Through the use of lift-platform industrial trucks and skids, the latter being platforms on legs, with a

Materials Handling

clearance of 7, 9, or 11 inches beneath, packaged items in bags or boxes and materials received in units, as well as innumerable kinds of manufactured parts, can be handled by piling them on the skids. These skids are then picked up by running the truck beneath them, raising the truck platforms by a hydraulic mechanism until the skid legs clear the floor, and then carrying the load to its destination and setting it down.

More recently, the fork truck and pallet method of doing this same work has come into wide use. The pallet consists of two layers of boards, usually 1 inch thick and 6 inches wide, held apart by three 2 by 4 inch stringers to form a double-faced platform 6 inches in over-all height. Lengths and widths of these platforms may vary, but sizes now standardized for general use are 48 inches x 48 inches, 42 inches x 48 inches, and 36 inches x 36 inches, although other sizes such as 36 inches x 48 inches are often made.

To reduce weight and cost, especially for shipping materials from vendor to purchaser, pallets are now sometimes made of boards about ½ inch thick. "Expendable" pallets of heavy corrugated cardboard are also available, the stringers being replaced by cylinders or coils of the cardboard about 6 inches in diameter and 2 inches or more long, placed on end and spaced at suitable equal intervals in three rows each way. Single-faced pallets with boards on only one side of the stringers are also frequently used.

For shipment, loads of packaged or bagged items,

or items in units or bundles, are usually strapped on pallets, the common height of the loads being from 3 to 4 feet. For internal handling, the strapping is not used.

The pallets are handled by fork trucks, the fork consisting of two long prongs, raised and lowered by the truck, which run in between the pallet stringers and lift the load clear of the floor to carry it to its destination. Motor-driven trucks used for high lifting—battery or gasoline type—on which the operator rides, are equipped with a mast, up which the load can be lifted. This enables the load to be deposited on storage shelving or pallet racks, or, in the case of double-faced pallets, stacked on top of another load, so that the truck can pick up the two, or sometimes three, together.

In storage areas, these trucks with large, telescoping masts can stack as many as four loads, one on another, or to a total over-all height of about 22 feet, thus bringing into use a great amount of storage space above the floor level. Loads can be taken down by reversing the stacking operation.

Hand-operated fork trucks work on similar principles, but do not stack loads, this being done where necessary by a hand-operated stacker. These fork trucks are operated from the pulling handle for lifting and transportation of the load. Some are now motor-driven by push-button control in the handle for starting, moving forward or backward, and lifting or depositing loads. The operator walks but does not pull the load.

Materials Handling

The truck platform on which the load is carried is at the same time the fork itself. Toward the ends of the two prongs are mounted collapsible wheels. These are swiveled up into the fork prongs when the fork is run into a pallet. To support the load as the pallet is picked up and during transportation, the wheels are swiveled down to bear on the floor through wide gaps left between the bottom boards at each end of the bottom side of the pallet. These wheels are collapsed again for the withdrawal of the fork when the pallet is deposited.

Palletized loads are frequently built up in so-called "pallet patterns" for greater stability in handling. This is done by interlocking oblong-shaped cartons or bags by turning some of them in a regular pattern so that they project under others, thus resulting in the load being held in place by friction. For shipment, the loads are usually two-way strapped on pallets, and, to prevent loads from shifting during transit and crushing containers and contents, carloads may be either strapped or glued together. The pallet method cuts average loading and unloading time of box cars down from 3½ to 5 hours per car to ¾ to 1¼ hours.

6. *Detailed activities involved in materials handling.* Materials handling in the industrial plant involves a series of well-defined activities. These are as follows:

(a) Analyzing the handling operations of all kinds in connection with (1) receiving and storing of incoming materials, (2) moving materials through all production operations, including in some cases a filling or packaging operation and sometimes cartoning, (3) delivering finished products to finished stock room or warehouse, (4) moving them to the shipping department where they may be boxed or crated, and (5) loading them on the carrier for transportation to customer.

(b) Making recommendations for changes in layout. Deciding on handling methods and equipment to use for each kind of work to save the most time and money in these operations. Then, upon approval of the methods, ordering and installing equipment, and getting it into satisfactory operation.

(c) Checking on the correct use of the equipment, the results secured, and the savings brought about. Making adjustments that will better adapt the methods to the requirements of operations where experience indicates that improvements can be brought about.

(d) Integrating all the different kinds of materials-handling work into a coordinated system which is properly timed to keep all work moving on a high production schedule.

(e) Planning with the plant maintenance department for the regular inspection, lubrication, adjustment, and the necessary repairing and overhauling of all the different kinds of materials-handling equipment, such as cranes, conveyors, industrial tractor-trailer equipment, motor trucks, and plant railroad.

Materials Handling

(f) Operating a plant transportation system, if one is set up, for the regular pick up and delivery of materials at numerous stations throughout the manufacturing and stores departments, on both regular schedules and special orders.

(g) Keeping in touch with handling methods in other plants, and with new and improved equipment and methods featured in magazine articles, news items and advertising, and in the literature sent out by manufacturers of equipment.

7. *Organization for management of materials handling.* Large manufacturing organizations have recognized the pressing need for constant attention to efficiency and economy in materials handling, and to the effective discharging of the activities covered in this field. Many companies have set up special organizations for these purposes. One plan is to appoint a materials-handling committee with a general chairman in the headquarters plant, and a materials-handling engineer in charge of the work in each individual plant.

Under such a plan, the department in each plant works directly under the plant manager but also under the guidance of the central committee. Each engineer endeavors to develop, improve and adapt materials-handling methods, and to introduce equipment to bring about the highest production and lowest handling cost possible in his own plant. He is free to develop original ideas, and to carry on experiments.

All improvement that an engineer brings about are written up, together with the results of the installations, and are reproduced, with illustrations, for distribution throughout all plants. Even experiments that have failed are considered valuable information, and are likewise circulated to avoid repeating the same failures in other plants. In this manner, the entire organization gets the benefit of the developments of each materials-handling engineer, no matter where located.

The entire staff of materials-handling engineers throughout the company is organized into groups according to the particular specialties of the individual men. For example, some are put on conveyors, some on industrial trucks, some on cranes, and some on bulk handling. Each of these groups holds meetings several times a year, going to one or another of the plants for the meetings, and then inspecting the materials-handling methods and equipment of that plant.

Improvements and advances in practices and equipment are discussed on the basis of the various experiences, and conclusions and decisions are reached which are put into effect in all the plants of the company, wherever applicable. Thus, the entire company moves forward in materials-handling improvements and cost reduction as fast as anything new and good is discovered. The great economies and production advances thus brought about are of the utmost significance in holding down costs, and in increasing production rates for the organization as a whole.

Materials Handling

Within each plant, there are others engaged in materials-handling work. In the larger units, there are sometimes as many as a hundred men. Two methods are used in carrying on the local work. One method is to have all materials-handling activities under the jurisdiction of the local materials-handling engineer, with the engineer reporting to the plant manager as far as local operations are concerned.

The needs of the particular plant in getting out production come first in consideration. In this connection, the engineer is responsible for (a) analyses and recommendations, (b) equipment ordering and installation, (c) induction of operatives in the methods, (d) checking on operating and cost saving results and making improvements in the service, (e) integrating the systems into other materials-handling operations, (f) checking on maintenance, and (g) keeping track of materials-handling progress throughout the entire company, as well as throughout industry at large.

Actual operations of crane men, truckers, men supplying materials, and men attending to conveyor systems are under the local plant manager. He controls these men through his superintendent and foremen, or through his production planning and control engineer. He uses the latter in cases where materials handling is carried on directly as one of the production control service sections, such as storing materials and issuing and moving them to production centers.

General Electric, Westinghouse Electric, International Harvester, and other large companies which have made striking advances in materials-handling methods, operate under the plan of having a plant transportation section separate from the engineering work of materials handling. This plan has the advantage of separating operation from engineering as far as general administration is concerned, and of giving jurisdiction of the handling procedures and equipment to those whose main concern is production, for which the materials handling is done. The transportation job, moreover, is a large one which, if poorly run, will slow down or stop production lines—one of the most serious happenings in any mass production plant.

The alternative plan is to have the materials-handling engineer, who is concerned with analyses and improvements of materials-handling techniques, also operate the plant transportation system in moving materials into storage, into and through production, into and through finished stock rooms or warehouses, and into and through shipping. This system is based on the fact that a great deal of this work is continuous or repetitive, and is therefore a matter of easily managed routine. This is not too good a reason, however. The fact still remains that the work comes under operation, thus logically making it a function that would seem to be best administered by the production department whose work it serves.

8. *Materials-handling organization in small plants.* Small plants usually do not have the kind or volume of

Materials Handling

production, or the size of staff, to enable them to break down responsibilities so that men can give full-time consideration to special duties. Materials-handling operations, therefore, must necessarily be only a part-time consideration of some supervisor, and hence, by force of circumstances, often suffers from neglect.

The best way for the management of a small plant to take care of this situation is to appoint some capable man—say the industrial engineer, production planning supervisor, or plant engineer—to take over the responsibility of materials handling and give a definite portion of his time to the task. He, in turn, will do well to select one of his assistants, often a younger man, to specialize in this field. At times, a consultant or a materials-handling representative may be called in for advice, as a means of avoiding expensive errors and useless experiments. By making use of such a plan, the management of a small plant is almost certain to find that any costs involved will be far outweighed by the advantages derived.

Review

What percentage of the cost of manufacturing goes for the handling of materials and products in an industrial plant?

Give some of the rules that should be followed in providing for efficient materials handling.

What are some of the economies that may be obtained by efficient materials handling?

What types of equipment are used for moving materials in a factory?

Describe the lift truck.

What are some of the activities involved in managing materials-handling operations?

Describe a form of organization which may be set up for the management of materials handling.

CHAPTER XIII

Engineering and Manufacturing Design

1. *The function of the engineering department.* In the manufacturing of products, it is the function of the engineering department to discover the features which must be incorporated into the design of the products in order to create a large enough demand to enable the company to sell the products in a sufficient volume to produce a profit. When the products are for special orders, the design must fulfill the particular customer's requirements.

In other words, when the sales department of a manufacturing company sees the need for improving a current product or developing a new product, or bringing in special orders from customers, it is the function of the engineering department to work out the new design so that the product will have the characteristics and qualities which the prospective purchaser is most likely to demand. It is also the function of the engineering department to design the product so that it can be manufactured by the company in the simplest manner possible and at the lowest reasonable cost.

It is definitely advisable for the engineering department to explore the possibility of designing the product so that it can be made on the equipment currently in use in the plant. If this can be done, it will result in lower manufacturing costs, which may be essential to the marketing of the product, particularly if the product is one which will meet with keen competition, or will be hard to introduce. Investment in new equipment is not usually advisable until some idea is obtained as to the possible success of the product on the market.

2. *Improvement of products.* A manufacturing company may have successfully designed and produced a product which has found a wide market, but it is by no means certain that the company can easily hold this market exclusively. Rival products are most likely to appear to compete with the company's product. While patent laws may prevent outright duplication of a product, the patent can seldom be so exclusive as to close the market entirely to competition. Consequently, it is necessary for a company to endeavor continually to improve its product, or to develop a new product to take its place.

This fact is well illustrated in the manufacture of materials-handling equipment. Some time ago, one company produced a hydraulically operated grab for the handling of baled materials by fork trucks. Presumably, the patent papers were carefully drawn up, but scarcely six months had elapsed before other companies adopted the basic idea and were producing grabs of

Engineering and Manufacturing Design 219

other designs which not only served the same purposes, but had improved features.

3. *Basic conception of engineering.* Basically, an engineering department is supposed to be able to design for successful manufacture either brand new products, or products that are superior to any similar products previously produced. For a time, a product may stand as it was originally designed, but eventually unpreventable competition is likely to necessitate a change. The engineering department must then discard its previous design and introduce an improved design to maintain the company's market.

If competitors later follow suit, as they are likely to do, the company may meet this new development by following one of two courses. One course is for the engineering department to simplify the design so as to cut manufacturing costs and thus enable the company to stay ahead of its competitors. The other course is for the company to drop the product in question and have its engineering department bring out some other product which will find a wide market and be able to stave off new competition for a considerable time.

4. *Importance of methods engineering.* It is becoming increasingly recognized that the methods engineer—whatever may be his specific title—can be of great aid in assisting the engineering department to develop designs which can be produced without difficulty on the company's equipment. The methods engineer can also be of much help in converting a customer's design into

a more workable form so that the product can be made more quickly and economically than if the original design were followed.

The methods engineer is in a position to take the original designs of his company's products, or the designs of customer companies, and assist in translating these designs into production possibilities with the simplest manufacturing methods and the lowest obtainable manufacturing costs consistent with the quality of the product. He can do this because his data and records on production procedures, and his intimate acquaintance with his company's facilities and methods provide him with the means of working out manufacturing procedures which are both realistic and economical.

Successful manufacturing today depends to a large extent on a concern's ability to convert engineering conceptions into production actualities in a relatively short time. Consequently, every manufacturing company needs to develop and maintain a forward-looking engineering department which not only can devise marketable products, but can design them so that they may be economically produced.

5. *Tie-in of product design with manufacturing processes.* In redesigning an existing product or designing a new product, it is important that the engineering department check on the company's manufacturing facilities, and adapt its designs according to the requirements and limitations of existing equipment.

Engineering and Manufacturing Design 221

For example, a part that may be designed for manufacture in one piece may have to be redesigned to be produced in two or more parts if the machines in the plant are not of a kind to permit one-piece processing. While new equipment may be purchased that will make such a piece on one machine, the initial cost of this machine may far outweigh any cost-saving advantages of the new equipment, unless the part is to be manufactured under continuous mass production, or the machine can be used for making other products.

A convenient method for calculating the economies which may be derived from installing new manufacturing equipment, instead of continuing to use existing equipment, is given in an extensive study published by William A. Kelly of the Machinery and Allied Products Institute. Under this method, the existing equipment is called the "defender" and the proposed new equipment is designated as the "contender."

In applying the method, a calculation is made of the costs of manufacturing and the rate of output under the current and the proposed equipment. This indicates basically how long a time will elapse before the reduced costs under the new equipment will save a sufficient amount of money to return the purchase price of installing it. If it seems likely that the improved machinery will return its cost in a reasonable time, say two years, it is usually advisable to buy it.

6. *Designing sales appeal into manufactured products.* In designing modern manufactured products, success-

ful companies give careful attention to the appearance of the products as well as to their utilitarian functions. For example, equipment used in stores, offices, public buildings, and other locations where it is visible to a large number of persons, is particularly designed for attractive appearance as well as for efficient operation. This trend has spread even to manufacturing equipment which today is often designed not only for efficient low-cost operation, but also for the purpose of making the equipment fit in harmoniously with the surroundings in which it is used.

Many companies in their manufacturing departments use paint of the proper colors to help the operators see their work more closely and thus aid in relieving them from eye strain, consequent tension, and undue fatigue. In addition to the use of modern lighting equipment, better lighting is secured at the work place by the painting of machines in colors which not only distinguish between operating areas and machine frameworks but also have higher reflection value without glare, and therefore increase the intensity of illumination at the point of operation. As a further means of eliminating glare, suitable colors are also used on walls and floors.

7. *Tooling for production.* A good policy is to plan the tooling for a product at the time the product is being designed. The designers will then have some ideas of how to develop the various parts of the product so that tooling costs will be as low as possible. Tools, jigs and

Engineering and Manufacturing Design 223

fixtures must be designed for the proper holding and fabrication of the various parts of the product. If the tools for one product can be used directly, or with slight adaptations, in the manufacture of other products, the tooling costs of jobs will be lowered. It is a waste of money for tool and fixture designers to develop these facilities for a new job when existing tooling for previous jobs may answer the purpose for the new job, either directly or by making slight adaptations.

Money can also be saved by designing tools, jigs and fixtures, and by developing parts or kinds of equipment which can be profitably substituted for existing equipment. For example, in certain cutting-off operations, a great advantage was derived from abandoning the use of a toothed band saw and substituting a straight band of steel without teeth, since the life of the plain cutting bands proved to be ten times that of the toothed bands. Furthermore, the original cost of the plain bands was only a fraction of the toothed bands.

8. *Testing.* Many manufactured products, especially those made to a particular order, must undergo testing before they will be accepted by the customer. Such testing is particularly necessary in the case of many kinds of equipment for manufacturing or power-producing purposes. Manufacturing contracts may call for specific kinds of performances under stated conditions and the purchaser will not accept the equipment unless it meets all such specifications, or he may pay more, or less, for the equipment depending upon

whether it exceeds stipulated performance, or falls below such performance.

Power-plant equipment represents one class in which performance testing is the basis for the payment of bonuses for higher-than-specified performance efficiency, or for a proportionate reduction in the stipulated payment if the performance efficiency of the equipment falls below the specifications. Obviously, an engineering department designing such equipment strives to have the performance above par, if this can be accomplished at no considerably extra cost, and will result in relatively higher bonuses in payment for the equipment.

9. *Installation.* Many companies which make specialized equipment, such as that used in power plants, rolling mills, and many branches of heavy manufacturing, do the installing of the equipment and run the tests, where tests are required. The large companies which supply customers with pressurized gases, such as acetylene, often design and install the equipment necessary for the use of these gases under conditions which meet all safety and fire prevention requirements.

10. *Supplying data to manufacturing departments.* Engineering departments not only design products and the parts entering into them, but also furnish certain important information needed by the production control department. Among these items are bills of material which list all the parts required for one unit of the complete product: the number of each of such parts for

Engineering and Manufacturing Design

one assembled unit; the materials of which the various parts are made; the drawings upon which the parts are shown; and all other information required for the production of one unit of the product. Operation sheets are often worked out in the production control department, particularly in the case of newly designed products.

The engineering department does the designing of the products to be manufactured and therefore has all the fundamental information in regard to these products. The production control department and the manufacturing department must familiarize themselves with this information so as to perform their respective functions in the manufacture of the product.

During the initial manufacturing of a new product, many questions usually arise in regard to production control procedures and actual manufacturing operations. Many questions are also likely to come up as to the reasons for particular designs, for the use of particular metals or other materials, for the methods of operation or use of the equipment or product, and for many other things of like nature. The answers to all these questions must be supplied by the engineering department, or worked out by the members of this department in collaboration with the production control and manufacturing departments.

Once the product is under manufacture, the engineering department will have very little to do with the manufacturing operations except in the position of "trouble shooter" when new questions come up. But the responsibility for keeping the product up to date rests with the engineering department. Consequently, provision is usually made, especially by the larger companies, for checks and surveys of the company's products in use in plants or by consumers. By this method, the company keeps informed as to what improvements need to be made to keep the products, whatever their nature, up to date and in line with the customers' demands.

11. *Use of new manufacturing methods and equipment.* Because of the rapid advance in manufacturing methods and equipment, it is imperative that a plant keep pace with modern developments and follow up all sources of information within its field so as to introduce improved production facilities whenever economically advisable. Die casting has developed at a rapid rate and has cut the cost of many products formerly produced by machining operations. Welding has superseded much of the former bolting and riveting. Whole sections of airplanes are now fabricated in operations on large presses, thereby increasing the strength of the product and cutting down the labor formerly required in processing and assembling smaller parts.

Review

Describe the function of the engineering department of a company.

What two courses may a company follow in order to maintain its market in the face of competition?

Engineering and Manufacturing Design

Name some of the important duties of the methods engineer.

In designing a product, why should the engineering department be familiar with the company's existing equipment?

Describe a method which may be used to determine whether or not new equipment should be purchased.

What factor besides efficient operation needs to be taken into consideration today in designing equipment?

Why is the proper use of paint on equipment, walls and floors advantageous to the functioning of manufacturing departments?

How can money be saved in tooling for production?

Under what conditions do engineering departments strive to design equipment which will have higher-than-specified performance efficiency?

Give an example of the kind of information which the engineering department furnishes the production control department.

CHAPTER XIV

Tooling and Automation

1. *Definitions.* Many different kinds of implements come under the general classification of tools as is indicated by the following list:

Tool: any implement used in the doing of work. In manufacturing plants, the term relates more specifically to cutting appliances, although the designation covers hammers, mallets and other non-machining tools.

Fixtures: a device in which work is held while under processing.

Jig: a holding device provided with a guide or guides—such as a bushing—to spot the operation.

Die: a press tool for blanking, cutting, punching, forming, shearing or stamping sheet metal. It is also a molding device used in presses for forming soft metals, molten metals or plastics.

Arbor: a device in the form of a spindle for holding tools during a cutting operation.

Mandrel: a holding mechanism on which parts that have been bored are held during lathe operations.

Tooling and Automation

Socket, collet, sleeve: adapters for fitting cutting tools into holding devices for a machining operation.

Gage—external or internal: a measuring instrument for checking the conformance of machined surfaces or diameters to specified dimensions. There are external and internal gages. Some are of the dual type—"go" and "no go"—to check parts to be held between limits.

2. *Determining tool requirements.* For any work requiring the use of machine tools—standard or special—such as milling machines, shapers, planers, hobbing machines and drill presses, it is necessary to provide tools which are adequate for the doing of the work. These tools must be so constructed that they can be used to process parts to close and often highly accurate dimensions, sometimes to the ten-thousandth of an inch. Most machine tools are made so that different tools may be used in them to perform many different kinds of work.

When a new metal product is to be manufactured, the first step is to have the company's engineering or drafting department design it according to certain specifications which designate the requirements to be met. If the product is to be a special one for a particular customer, the customer will have stated his requirements and may have even supplied drawings for the product. In many cases, these drawings are modified by agreement of the two parties to improve the product, simplifying the design, and cut the manufacturing costs.

After the design of the product is fixed, drawings are made of all the parts which are designed not only for their particular purposes, but also for convenience and low cost of manufacture. When the drawings have been completed, the product or process engineer makes a comprehensive analysis of the methods for manufacturing the product.

At the same time, the tool engineer, or whoever heads up the tool-making department, analyzes the drawings to develop and produce any special tools that may be needed in manufacturing the product. In case there are optional methods of manufacture, the tool engineer confers with the process engineer in order to find out what particular manufacturing procedures are to be adopted. If certain work is to be subcontracted to outside companies, a tooling study of such work is not necessary.

In case the tools are to be designed and produced by the company, or made outside according to the company's designs, it is necessary for the tool engineer to know through what manufacturing processes and equipment the parts are to be put, so that he may design the tools accordingly. Care must be exercised, however, in the choice of types of equipment and processes through which the parts must pass during manufacture, or the cost of tooling and processing may be excessive and thus result in the job producing a smaller profit than the amount which should be earned.

3. *Tooling.* Many of the operations in metal-working and wood-working plants require the use of small tools to cut, shape, mill, drill and otherwise fashion the products under manufacture. Numerous varieties of hand tools are needed for many of the jobs, such as hammers, saws, drills and screwdrivers. On machines fashioning a wide variety of wood products, saws, planing cutters and wood-milling cutters are required. Machines processing metal parts use such tools as drills, reamers, milling cutters, planer tools, dies, shears, punches and grinding wheels.

Many of the tools required are standard products of the tool manufacturing companies and can be obtained from the stocks of dealers or manufacturers. For a considerable portion of manufacture, however, special tools are needed. Many companies have tool designing and manufacturing departments to develop the tooling for specific jobs. Other companies have their tools designed and produced by one of the many companies engaged in tool manufacture.

The tooling investment for the production of the parts to be used in the manufacture of a product may be as high as 10 per cent of the final unit cost of making the product, according to studies made in the General Aniline and Film Corporation by Paul T. Sherwood. Writing on this subject in *Systems Magazine* (Sept. 1952, p. 17), Mr. Sherwood points out that product design should coordinate with economical tooling and production, and tool design and production, in turn, must coordinate with a determination of manufacturing methods and tooling requirements. Changes in product design may later modify or retire existing tooling.

4. *Tool control.* A highly important factor in connection with the use of tools is a system for controlling their issue and use. The general supply stores department of the General Aniline and Film Corporation has installed a complete system of tool control records to account for over 6,000 jigs, dies and templates, and about 2,500 items in expendable tools. A Kardex locater file, indexed numerically by tool number, is used to record the non-expendable tooling, such as dies, jigs, and templates, kept in the tool storeroom. The card gives tool number, description and bin location.

A signature file is kept of all department heads who are authorized to requisition tools, stating the various groupings under which the signer is authorized to make requisitions. Requisition slips are presented when tools are to be withdrawn, and these slips are held in a Kolect-A-Matic pocket while the tools are at the job. When the tools are returned, the issue slips are given back to the signers. The date the tool is returned is the only entry made on the record card, since the issue slip tells where the tool is when out.

The tool inventory is checked during the course of each year, about one-twelfth of the tool storeroom being covered per month.

Tooling and Automation

5. *Automatic machinery.* In recent years, the trend has been toward developing higher automaticity in industrial operations. Many new types of machines have been designed and built in which the work is processed through cycles of operations controlled by cams or other automatic operating devices.

In using such machines, the operator has merely to insert a part in a fixture, start the machine, and do the same for one or more additional machines. He then removes the part from the first machine, replaces the part with another one of the same kind, and similarly attends to the other machines in the same order as he first started them. Such machines can be constructed so as to stop automatically in case the operator may be delayed in removing and replacing the part. Under such a plan, where the work cycle occupies a considerable time, the operator can often tend quite a number of machines working on the same or different kinds of parts.

An advanced development has been the designing and manufacturing of automatic machines for performing a cycle of operations on parts. The operator has merely to put each part into a fixture on the machine and remove it when it has been processed through the cycle of operations and returns to the original point where it was placed in the fixture. The machine indexes the parts successively to the different work stations and all operations are timed for synchronized machining.

Many machines have been developed for entirely automatic operation, such as braiding machines, cabling machines, chain-link assembling machines, and machines for producing welded pipe. In the case of such machines, all that the operator has to do is to supply additional material when the supply drops down to the replenishment point.

In automotive plants, operations on many machines are performed automatically. For example, in fabricating sheet metal to form car body parts, a sheet from one operation will be picked up by metal grippers and swung to a certain angle from which, upon release by the grippers, it will fall into position for the next operation. The term "automation" is applied to operations of this and similar kinds, and the process is being increasingly applied in many industries to replace former hand operations.

Where a large production of parts through a continous series of standard operations is necessary over a long period, it has been found profitable in certain plants to arrange machines in the sequence of operations and connect them by materials-handling equipment which transfers the fixtures holding the parts successively from operation to operation until the full series has been completed. The operations are regulated by a master electrical control which stops the conveyor and positions the work at each station, actuates the manufacturing equipment simultaneously, performs the work at each station, releases the work fixtures simul-

Tooling and Automation

taneously after each operation, and allows the conveyor to move them on to the next station.

At the end of the production line, an operator removes the parts from the fixtures, and returns the latter on a conveyor to the operator at the head of the line who reloads the fixtures, and again puts them on the conveyor line. A signal board is usually set up with such installations. If any trouble develops at an operating station, a light will flash on, thus enabling a repairman to know at once where the difficulty is located.

Automatic production such as this is being used at the Westinghouse plant in Columbus, Ohio. Here, 2,613 machines and more than 25 miles of conveyor line combine to produce two refrigerators a minute. The machines blank out the steel, shear it, coat it with a drawing compound, draw, form, notch, trim, pierce and weld. Other machines position the refrigerators as they pass through the assembly line to final inspection.

Companies which manufacture the many kinds of machine tools needed for the mass production of innumerable industrial and commercial products have devised production lines of the foregoing type, and have thus brought about huge cost reductions in machining operations. One of the original installations at a large manufacturing plant was set up to machine aircraft cylinder heads. It produced a finished cylinder head every 48 seconds. The cost of the machine was $250,000. This cost was returned in six months because of the high production and the greatly reduced handling of parts brought about by the integrated machine.

6. *Automation.* A more recent and highly important development is that known as automation. This concept envisions a type of equipment which is self-controlled throughout. Its ultimate aim is the automatic factory, approach to which has already been achieved at the present time.

In the automotive field, where automation has made some of its greatest progress, long-run, constant demand items are being produced almost entirely by machines. At one Ford Company engine plant, for example, human hands place an engine block casting on a 350-foot-long machine which takes over and performs more than five hundred operations of various kinds, and finally inspects the finished block.

In its simpler forms, automation is applied to cycles of operations that are regulated by means of a pre-punched tape run through an electronic control mechanism which actuates the processing tools. This procedure has been termed "programming." Research in this field has been carried on at the Graduate School of Business Administration of Harvard University, and rapid progress has been made in the development of these types of almost unbelievable kinds of equipment.

In a paper summarizing these developments (Abstract from a report on "Machine Controls That Remember" by C. J. Jacoby, 3rd, D. R. Aufderhoide, R. B. Keller, P. L. Nies and G. P. Tanquary, appearing in "Mechanical Engineering," Vol. 74, No. 10) the author,

C. J. Jacoby, 3rd, explains the accomplishments attained, as follows:

> Programming—the direction of a mechanism through a desired operating cycle—is the term given to a development which makes possible automatically controlled general-purpose machines. . . . Through the use of mechanical aids, such as templates, cams, limit switches and the like, the programming of the cutting-tool travel does not have to be done by the human operator. . . . However, the programming is built into the machine and the program cannot be changed to produce a different product without substantial time being taken to change the controlling elements. . . .
>
> The lack of flexibility in such machines can be overcome by utilizing programming information from some external source, which is fed into the machine tool to control the operation automatically. . . . Consider a Cincinnati Hydrotel vertical-spindle milling machine . . . which has been adapted to program control by the Servomechanisms Laboratory of the Massachusetts Institute of Technology. This control has the ability to coordinate tool motion along each of three axes. The shape to be cut is defined by a series of points in space and the cutting tool is directed from one point to the next point at the desired feed rate by means of information stored on a punched tape. These points may be as close together as 0.0005 inch or as far apart as 60 inches.
>
> The direction of the cutting tool by servomech-

anisms insures that the actual position of the cutting tool corresponds at all times with the instructed position. Thus with coordinated control of three axes of motion, it is possible to approximate any desired shape—a circle, an irregular path, or a straight line—while the control of the time from point to point permits control at the rate of feed at all times.

The preparation of the tape requires the analysis of the part to be produced and determination of the various tools and cutting feeds to be used, as must be done in setting up a standard machine tool. The best path of the cutting tool is then determined, and the points and cutting rates must be translated into coordinate axis positions and times, and the tape punched. This can be systematized and performed by clerical help.

A simplified control could be made for use in controlling motion in only two axes. . . .

The most obvious use of such a control lies in the production of accurate, complex shapes. The movement along each axis is punched, step by step in the tape when it is made, but the machine when controlled by the tape operates at the desired cutting rate. This results in a minimum of human error and products of uniform quality. There is no need to make a cut, measure, and make another cut until the desired size is achieved. This is recorded on the tape, and the cutting tool is moved to that position with an accuracy of plus or minus 0.0005 inch.

The point of actual cutting is determined by the diameter of the cutting tool and it must be considered when making the tape. This requires the use of the correct size tool if accurate reproduction is to be obtained. Tool wear will change the diameter and thus will introduce inaccuracies. Ordinarily, this tool wear would not excessively reduce the accuracy of reproduction, but the worn tool would have to be resharpened and issued to another job requiring the next smaller "standard" size tool.

Although the use of programming controls may result in increased production per machine-hour, an important feature is the reduction of the human attention and skill needed. Since the control of the machine is automatic, the function of the operator is to load, unload and start the machine. Therefore, he is able to operate several machines and the labor cost per piece is reduced. Furthermore, a skilled machinist is no longer required to operate the machine.

Analysis of a few parts—chosen to be typical of machine shop operations—indicates that substantial savings are possible. . . . Project engineers at M.I.T. estimate that their control could be produced and installed at a price roughly comparable to that of the machine it would control. There is no doubt that initial capital outlay for programming controls will be large. Yet, the increased productivity per machine-hour quite conceivably could result in the same or even less capital investment per unit of output.

. . . This role of the maintenance man becomes increasingly important since programming controls are complex instruments. The preparation of the tape, although final computations and actual preparations are routine and may be performed by clerical personnel, will require men skilled in the use of programming controls. . . . The engineering departments will have to be more closely coordinated with production, as the design of a part will influence greatly its adaptability to programming controls. . . .

Can the same controls be used to operate loading, positioning, and conveyors joining the machines to achieve automation? Technically, the answer is, definitely, yes!

It would not be feasible to use the mechanical types of automation for the production of several different products, similar in size and shape and going through similar sequences of operations, as the volume of production of each product could not absorb the necessary set-up cost. . . .

Automatic loading and positioning devices for each machine could be operated by the programming control and the parts moved from machine to machine by conveyors. The synchronization of individual machines could be accomplished by means of electrical impulses at the end of each tape operation, stopping the individual machine, and closing a switch in a starting circuit. The starting circuit would become activated when all the switches in the circuit were closed—thus starting the machines on a new cycle. No set-up time would be required for a model change, except the threading of new tapes in the individual programming controls. Or perhaps

Tooling and Automation

the machines would be joined by a transfer machine-type conveyor which serves the dual function of transporting the workpiece from operation to operation and of holding the workpiece during the machining operations. . . .

On the other hand, it would seem dubious that programming controls would be used to produce large quantities of identical products, when the automotive companies have demonstrated that the job can be done effectively with relatively less-expensive electric circuits utilizing limit switches and mechanical interlocks. The flexibility inherent in programming controls is just not required in large volume production.

Programming controls are not the one answer to automation, or even to automaticity. Electric circuits utilizing limit switches and mechanical interlocks will always have a major part to play. However, where flexibility of operations is necessary, programming controls will come to play an increasingly important role, both in application to general purpose, machinery and to flexible, but more specialized machinery used in producing a line of products.

7. *Factories that run themselves.* The ultimate in automation would be a factory where one could feed raw materials in at one end, throw a switch, and ultimately remove the final product from the other end. In the chemical and petroleum industries, great strides have been made in this direction. But automobile manufacture, where the end product is composed of many

individual units, poses a tougher problem. Automation on automobile production lines requires specialized handling devices and complex machines and conveyors. Practical experts, when talking of 100 per cent automation, say that it will eventually come. It may not be just around the corner, but with planning, engineering and training begun now, automatic factories will increase in the years immediately ahead.

Under conditions today, machines generally become obsolete as soon as the need for a particular product is at an end. The machines of the automatic factory, however, would have a functional design, which would take into account the operations as well as the end product. These operations would be highly specialized units linked together electronically and more flexible than those known today.

The Brown-Leaver theory is that all manufacturing operations can be reduced to a few basic functions, with a standard machine packaged to perform each function. The fully automatic factory requires basic types of machine units, all of which exist today.

First, there must be devices to give and receive information. These already exist in dozens of forms. For example, photo-electric cells are used to "see" for checking purposes; vibration pickups are installed for detecting differences in pressure; punch card systems are employed for recording and repeating information; almost incredible electronic-tube counters are used to make calculations.

Tooling and Automation

The second class of basic machine unit is an electronic device which accepts information fed into it, and then feeds controlled power to the machines that actually make products. There are many examples of these machines in operation today.

The third class of machine units perform actual manufacturing operations, as for example, the automatic screw machine. In most cases, industry has used automatic machines to do specialized jobs. Under the Brown-Leaver arrangement, a number of such machines are combined in series to perform all the operations required to produce and assemble a complete product. This complete machine is highly adaptable; its components can easily be rearranged to make an entirely different product.

The advent of the automatic factory has brought sociological problems to the fore, and it is vitally necessary to lay the groundwork for their eventual solution. It is management's responsibility to regulate the rate at which such devices are introduced so as not to introduce these new developments at a faster rate than they can be absorbed into the manufacturing economy without detriment to employment opportunities for workers.

Review

Describe some of the different kinds of implements that come under the general classification of tools.

What factors need to be taken into consideration in determining tool requirements?

Describe a system for controlling the issue and use of tools.

Describe the operations of three types of automatic machinery now in use.

What is meant by "automation" and what is its ultimate aim?

What basic types of machine units will be required by the fully automatic factory?

What problem would be created by the too-fast development of automatic factories?

CHAPTER XV

Motion and Time Study

1. *Definitions.* Motion and time study has been defined as a searching, scientific analysis of methods and equipment used, or planned for, in doing a piece of work. It further includes development in practical detail of the best manner of doing the work, and determination of the time required.

Job analysis is the study of industrial operations and conditions by the use of scientific methods. The making of a job analysis enlists the closely associated techniques of motion and time study.

Motion study is concerned with the study of human and mechanical motions. It seeks to eliminate wasteful moves and fatigue wherever possible, and to arrange the motions of an operation in their best possible sequence for rhythm and efficiency on the part of the operator.

Time study logically goes along with motion study. It is the science of observing and recording the time required to perform each element of an operation.

2. *Purpose of motion and time study.* While the aims of motion and time study may be variously stated, there

are really four fundamental purposes behind all such studies. These are as follows:

(a) To determine the "one best way" of doing a task, together with its proper elapsed time.
(b) To secure times for planning.
(c) To obtain times for cost estimating and budget purposes.
(d) To serve as a basis for the setting of fair wage standards, particularly in respect to piecework rates and bonuses.

Motion and time study is so closely associated with the setting of piecework rates and bonuses that other and perhaps more important reasons have been overlooked. Most important of these is to determine the *best way of doing the job,* for, in improving the method of operation, lies the greatest opportunity for the reduction of cost and the increase of production.

3. *Elements of motion and time study.* It is obvious that standard performance will not be possible unless the conditions under which the operation is performed are standardized. Motion and time studies, therefore, in order to fulfill their purposes, must consider the operation, material, equipment, methods, working conditions, the work place and the workman. The following steps, listed by Lowry, Maynard and Stegomerten, are considered essential in making a motion and time study:

(a) Preliminary analysis and standardization:
  (1) Choice of operator.

Motion and Time Study

    (2) Approaching and securing operator's co-operation.
    (3) Purpose of operation.
    (4) Inspection standards.
    (5) Materials.
    (6) Set-up and preparation time.
    (7) Method.
    (8) Machine and tools.
    (9) Jigs and fixtures.
    (10) Working conditions.

(b) Making time studies:
    (1) Making motion studies.
    (2) Taking stop-watch readings.
    (3) Gathering complete "job" information.
    (4) Gathering complete "man" information.

(c) Analyzing time studies and setting standard times:
    (1) Arithmetical computations.
    (2) Allowance for skill and effort.
    (3) Allowance for fatigue, personal needs, breakdowns, etc.

(d) Developing routine procedure that will insure the accomplishment of the work and permanence of the working conditions:
    (1) Compilation of instruction cards.
    (2) Making information available to foremen and workers.
    (3) Developing clerical routine.

(e) Determining the financial incentive which will serve to interest the worker in the performance of the standard.

There are two fundamental methods in general use for making a motion and time study. One is the stopwatch method. In other words, readings are taken with a decimal stop watch mounted in a time-study board. The other method is known as the micromotion method, which consists of taking moving pictures of the operation. In this case, the time reading is registered on the film by means of a large, fast-moving clock in the background, with a dial divided into 100 parts, and a hand making 20 revolutions per minute, thus giving readings to one two-thousandths of a minute.

4. *Preliminary analysis and standardization.* In formulating a standard time, the aim should be to set such a time as can be equaled or slightly excelled by the average man working at average effort and under average conditions. The exceptional operator should be able to make considerably faster time and hence a larger bonus. The poor worker should not be able to achieve the standard unless he improves his skill and effort.

In selecting an operator, the time study analyst should go to the department in which the study is to be taken and consult the foreman. The foreman represents the management, and he is usually interested in having standards correctly set. He will aid the analyst in selecting the particular machine and operator to be studied. It is considered good practice to select a highly skilled operator, because the rhythm and efficiency which such an operator displays in performing his task are of great help in analyzing the job.

Motion and Time Study

The operator should be told of the purpose of the study, his fullest cooperation should be sought, and the time study should be openly made. Not only must the time-study man be a good diplomat, but he must also be familiar with shop operations so that workers will not be able to "put one over" on him.

5. *Analyzing the job.* The analyst should first fully acquaint himself with the purpose of the operation. To know why an operation is performed, and what function the finished part will play in the final assembly, often helps in eliminating useless operations.

From the engineering drawings, and by cooperation with the inspector, the analyst should then study the inspection standards of the job. The piece may be inspected immediately following the operation, or it may receive inspection later on in its process of manufacture.

Material specifications should be checked. For example, castings should be of normal consistency. If they are too hard, oversize, or difficult to machine, standard times cannot be properly set. Other materials should be checked in a similar manner.

The time required for setting up the job, reading of blueprints, getting instruction cards, and the like, should also be noted. These factors all add to the overall time and must be included for correct setting of standards, fixing of wage rates and scheduling of jobs.

Many plants have methods departments which make a study of machine procedures, set-ups and tools, and furnish this information to the time-study department. Combining this information with his own experience, the time-study man can arrive at a proper method of procedure. This involves a check-up on the speeds and feeds of the machines, the jigs and fixtures used, and the general working conditions at the production center. Every effort should be made to get the job running correctly before any timings are taken. When procedures and conditions are once set and timed, they become standard for that job and must be so maintained if the standard time is to be met in doing the work.

6. *Making time studies.* The equipment for making time studies usually consists of a decimal stop watch mounted in a time-study observation board, a speed counter for counting machine revolutions, and a supply of time-study observation sheets. One of these sheets is fastened to the observation board, which is held in the left arm of the observer, the watch being directly under the control of his left hand.

In place of a stop watch, use may be made of a "wink counter" which resembles a machine counter and reads to 1/2000 minute. A Marstochron may likewise be substituted. This instrument has two keys which, when depressed to register times, record pen lines on a traveling paper tape. These times are later read off by means of a scale.

In making timings, the observer first watches the operator go through several performances to make

Motion and Time Study

certain that the procedure is correct. When this is satisfactory, the observer breaks down the operation into its elements, gaging this process by elements in similar lines of work and by the natural pauses and rhythms of the operator, and then records these elements on the time-study sheet. Much more than that, however, is involved in making a thorough motion and time study. The following is an illustration of the full procedure which is required of an observer:

(a) Secure the cooperation of the worker.
(b) Obtain all necessary information, and record it on observation sheet.
(c) Divide the operation into its elements and list them on observation sheet.
(d) Record time of day and start the watch.
(e) Record data by the continuous method.
(f) Record time of day at end of study.
(g) Check all information; make sure that it is accurate and complete.
(h) Rate skill, effort, consistency of operator, and working conditions.
(i) Compute average and base times.
(j) Determine allowances.
(k) Add in allowances to set standard time.

In reading a stop watch, two methods are in general use. One method is the continuous method; the other is the "snap-back" method.

In the continuous method, the watch is started at the beginning of the study and left running continuously, readings being taken at the end of each element by noting the time of the watch as the hand passes by. Thus, the total cumulative time is obtained at the end of each element. Consequently, to obtain the actual lapses of time, differences between successive elements must be taken. This method has the advantage of giving the complete over-all time by reading the stop watch at the beginning and end of the study, and thus checking the time-study man.

The "snap-back" method is performed by reading the time of each element, and then snapping back the watch hand by a slight pressure on the stem. An experienced operator, by using a quick-acting watch, can often use this method to advantage. While it is claimed that a certain amount of time is lost in snapping back the watch hand, such loss is insignificant if the elements are fairly long. For very short elements, this method is obviously unfitted.

The "snap-back" method has the advantage of reading the time of each element directly without the need of making subtractions. It also provides greater freedom on the part of the analyst in timing elements made "out of sequence." Even the best of operators sometimes change their sequences slightly. The direct-reading "snap-back" method makes such changes easy to follow, while under the continuous method much greater care must be exercised. Both methods are in wide use and each should be employed for the type of work for which it is best fitted.

Motion and Time Study

The observer usually takes readings on about ten cycles of the performance of the work in order to insure that he has obtained a complete cross-section of the operation. In this way, he is able to note delays, spoiled pieces and machine conditions, and to get average data on the job. Before leaving the work place, he must get complete information as to the speeds, feeds, and characteristics of the machine. He must make sketches of the piece being worked on, and obtain information for its complete identification. He must also secure all necessary information about the worker, who must be rated as to skill, effort and consistency.

With the readings thus completed, the observer may proceed to analyze his study and set the standard time. Certain subtractions and averages are first made that give numerical values for the elements. If the elements are machine times, they should be checked by computations using the specific speeds and feeds. These computed times should be the used, rather than the observed times.

The following representative procedure, using the continuous method of timing, provides an illustration:

(a) Subtract successive watch readings to obtain the time for each element. Record these values in the "time" columns on the observation sheet.

(b) Examine the time-study data carefully for abnormal values, and, if any are found, they should be circled and excluded from the computations.

(c) Add the individual times for each element and record the total in the corresponding vertical column on the first line under the heading "Summary."

Table 1

PERFORMANCE RATING TABLE

SKILL			EFFORT		
+0.15	A1	Superskill	+0.13	A1	Superskill
+0.13	A2		+0.12	A2	
+0.11	B1	Excellent	+0.10	B1	Excellent
+0.08	B2		+0.08	B2	
+0.06	C1	Good	+0.05	C1	Good
+0.03	C2		+0.02	C2	
0.00	D	Average	0.00	D	Average
−0.05	E1	Fair	−0.04	E1	Fair
−0.10	E2		−0.08	E2	
−0.16	F1	Poor	−0.12	F1	Poor
−0.22	F2		−0.17	F2	

CONDITIONS			CONSISTENCY		
+0.06	A	Ideal	+0.04	A	Perfect
+0.04	B	Excellent	+0.03	B	Excellent
+0.02	C	Good	+0.01	C	Good
0.00	D	Average	0.00	D	Average
−0.03	E	Fair	−0.02	E	Fair
−0.07	F	Poor	−0.04	F	Poor

Motion and Time Study

(d) Add the number of observations for each element and record on the next line under the total obtained in (c).

(e) Determine the selected time for each element by the *Average Method.*

$$\text{Selected Time} = \frac{\text{Total of Times}}{\text{Number of Observations}}$$

7. *Leveling factor.* The object of motion and time study is to set the final time in such a manner that the average worker can equal the standard time or better it. It should call for a pace that he can maintain day after day, year in and year out, without unnecessary fatigue or hardship. Since a highly skilled worker is usually studied, it is obvious that some forms of adjustment or "leveling" to the average basis becomes necessary.

Through study of many operators, a series of curves based upon skill and effort of operators were developed by Maynard, Lowry and Stagomerten. For practical purposes, these have been reduced to a Performance Rating Table. This is shown in Table 1.

The rating for skill and effort is made in accordance with the characteristics of these factors, under the classifications of poor, fair, average, good, excellent and "super." The following provides an illustration:

(a) Poor Skill:
    (1) New man or misfit.
    (2) Unfamiliar with work.
    (3) Uncertain of proper sequence of operations.

(4) Hesitates between operations.
(5) Makes many errors.
(6) Movements clumsy and awkward.
(7) Does not coordinate mind and hands.
(8) Lacks self-confidence.
(9) Cannot read drawings well.
(10) Unable to think for himself.

(b) Fair Skill:
(1) Misfit on job for long time.
(2) Comparatively new man.
(3) Follows proper sequence of operations without much hesitating.
(4) Somewhat clumsy and uncertain but knows what he is doing.
(5) Fairly familiar with equipment and surroundings.
(6) Plans ahead to some extent.
(7) Lacks full self-confidence.
(8) Loses time due to own blunders.
(9) Can read drawings fairly well.
(10) Gets same output with less effort than poor man.

(c) Average Skill:
(1) Works with reasonable accuracy.
(2) Has self-confidence.
(3) Is proficient at the work.
(4) Follows a set procedure regularly.
(5) Understands his tools and equipment.
(6) Plans ahead.
(7) Coordinates hand and mind.
(8) Reads drawings well.

Motion and Time Study

- (9) A little slow in motions.
- (10) Turns out satisfactory work.

(d) Good Skill:
- (1) Noticeably better than ordinary run of men.
- (2) Markedly intelligent.
- (3) Possesses good reasoning ability.
- (4) Responds readily to suggestion.
- (5) Needs little supervision.
- (6) Uses machine or tools to good advantage.
- (7) Fairly quick in motions.
- (8) Works correctly to specifications.
- (9) Can instruct others less skilled.
- (10) Possesses originality.

(e) Excellent Skill:
- (1) Precision of action.
- (2) Shows speed and smoothness in performance.
- (3) Thoroughly familiar with work.
- (4) Makes no mistakes.
- (5) Works accurately with little measuring or checking.
- (6) Operates his machine or tools to best advantage.
- (7) Can think out best methods for doing work.
- (8) Makes speed without sacrificing quality.
- (9) Has full self-confidence.
- (10) Designs labor-saving tools.

(f) Superskill:
- (1) The operator of excellent skill perfected.

- (2) Has been at work for years.
- (3) Naturally suited to the work.
- (4) Works like a machine.
- (5) Motions so quick and smooth that they are hard to follow.
- (6) Does not seem to have to think about what he is doing.
- (7) Knows and uses all best methods and short cuts.
- (8) Conspicuously the best worker of all.

(g) Poor Effort:
- (1) Obviously kills time.
- (2) Makes unnecessary trips for tools and supplies.
- (3) Makes two motions where one would do.
- (4) Fails to work systematically.
- (5) Has poor set-up or arrangement of work.
- (6) Lacks interest in work.
- (7) Does work more accurately than necessary.
- (8) Resents suggestions.
- (9) Purposely uses wrong or poor tools.
- (10) Works slowly and appears lazy.

(h) Fair Effort:
- (1) Same general tendencies but of less intensity.
- (2) Accepts suggestions grudgingly.
- (3) Fairly systematic but does not always follow the same sequence.
- (4) Still somewhat too accurate.
- (5) Makes job unduly hard.

Motion and Time Study

    (6) Lacks confidence in the time-study man.
    (7) Possibly affected by late hours, dissipation, or mental worries.
    (8) Does not use best tools.
    (9) Seems purposely somewhat ignorant of the work at hand.
    (10) Puts some energy into his work.
(i) Average Effort:
    (1) Better than fair; poorer than good.
    (2) Has good set-up.
    (3) Works steadily.
    (4) Plans ahead.
    (5) Somewhat doubts the fairness of the time-study man.
    (6) Works with good system.
    (7) Reduces lost motions.
    (8) Accepts suggestions but makes none.
    (9) Seems to hold back his best effort.
(j) Good Effort:
    (1) Little or no lost time.
    (2) Takes an interest in the work.
    (3) Takes no notice of the time-study man.
    (4) Works at best pace suited for endurance.
    (5) Follows a set sequence.
    (6) Conscientious about his work.
    (7) Has faith in time-study man.
    (8) Likes advice and makes suggestions.
    (9) Well prepared for job and has work place in good order.
(k) Excellent Effort:
    (1) Works fast.

(2) Uses head as well as hands.
(3) Takes keen interest in work.
(4) Receives and makes many suggestions.
(5) Reduces false motions to a minimum.
(6) Works systematically to best of his ability.
(7) Has utmost confidence in time-study man.
(8) Cannot keep up effort more than a few days.
(9) Endeavors to show superiority.
(10) Uses best equipment and methods available.

8. *How to determine a leveling factor.* Having already made an estimate of skill, effort, and conditions, while the operation was being studied, it remains to estimate consistency. If the variation in the times of the element, as found on the observation sheet, is wide, the rating for consistency will be poor. If the variation is slight, the rating will be perfect. (See Performance Rating Table.) Record the symbol and its corresponding numerical value on the observation sheet. The algebraic sum of these numerical values added to 1.0 will give the leveling factor which should be recorded. For example, if the observer has made the following estimates:

$$\text{Skill} - \text{good} - C1 = +.06$$
$$\text{Effort} - \text{excellent} - B2 = +.08$$
$$\text{Conditions} - \text{average} - D = .00$$
$$\text{Consistency} - \text{average} - D = .00$$

Motion and Time Study

the leveling factor becomes

$$1.00 + .06 + .08 + .00 = 1.14.$$

This leveling factor is then applied to the time of each element to get the so-called *base time*.

Base Time = Selected Time × Leveling Factor.

Assume that the time of an element is .05 minutes. Using the leveling factor of 1.14, the base time becomes:

.05 minutes × 1.14 = 5.70 minutes

In this manner, .70 of a minute is added to allow the average worker to make standard. In the meantime, the expert makes higher piecework or bonus earnings.

9. *Leveling and rating time studies.* The usual methods of leveling and rating time studies are based on the judgment of the observer. Unless his experience enables him to evaluate the speed of normal workers on the kind of job he is studying, he cannot rate the performance with any assurance of attaining accuracy.

Robert L. Morrow has proposed a synthetic method of leveling. According to this method, the time study is taken as usual, broken down into its elements, and the elements are compared with standard times. The percentage of variation of the actual times from the standards is determined, and the same percentage is applied to other times for which predetermined time standards are not available. Machine time is kept separate from handling time and can be checked with tables or charts supplied by the equipment manufacturers for various processes and different materials.

The leveling factor, applied to the man-controlled time elements is then calculated by this formula:

$$L = \frac{S}{A}$$

L = the leveling factor
S = the synthetic time value in minutes for the handling time elements
A = the actual time value in minutes for the same elements, from the study.

This leveling factor is applied to all actual time values for elements performed by the operator.

10. *Instruction cards.* With the base time computed, instruction cards are compiled. An example of the procedure here is as follows:

(a) List the elements of the operation, the tools, speeds, and feeds.
(b) Record and add the base times previously computed on the observation sheet.
(c) Determine the total allowance to be added to the base time. For example, assume the following

  Personal Allowance 3%
  Miscellaneous Allowance (including drill changes, counting work, etc.) 7%
  Incentive Allowance 5%
  Total Allowance 15%

(d) Compute the standard time per piece.

Standard Time =
Base Time − (% Allowance × Base Time)

Instruction cards should either be mounted on the operator's machine, or placed on the foreman's desk where they may be consulted at all times. Shop and clerical routine must be established to insure that the conditions under which the times were established are maintained. Once a standard time is set, it should *never be changed,* unless the method of performing the operation is changed. This principle is widely accepted, with many modern plants guaranteeing the rates, except in cases of actual changes in methods.

To interest the worker in the increase in production, which can be accomplished, a suitable plan of financial reward, such as a piecework rate or bonus, must be offered him. While time study goes deeper than merely setting times for rates of pay, it must be recognized that its success depends upon adequate financial rewards.

11. *Synthetic method of setting times.* It is not the purpose of time study to study each individual job, but rather to gather unit times that may be used in predicting future operations. Thus, Frederick W. Taylor found for a certain class of work that certain elements, such as chucking and loading, were constantly occurring. He standardized their times so that when a new job came through he could calculate the machine time from the speeds and feeds of the machine, and add to this time the standard unit-handling time required.

In this way, he built up a standard for the job without going near it with a stop watch. It was his theory that such unit times could be compiled for an entire industry. This ultimate purpose of time study, namely, predetermination and prediction, should never be lost sight of by management.

The building-up, or synthetic, method of setting times on jobs is now in regular use by many manufacturing companies. It is of particular advantage on special jobs, on work of a non-repetitive nature, and on operations involving only a short manufacturing cycle.

A typical illustration is given by R. M. Barnes in "Motion and Time Study":

Elemental Time Data for Sensitive Drills
Machine Manipulation Time

Classes:
  A. Drilling, one drill and no bushing.
  B. Drilling, placing and removing bushing.
  C. Drilling, placing and removing drill.
  D. Drilling, placing and removing drill and bushing.

ELEMENTS	A	B	C	D
1. Place bushing in jig	..	06	..	06
2. Place drill in chuck	..	..	04	04
3. Advance drill to work	04	04	04	04
4. Raise drill from hole	03	03	03	03
5. Remove bushing from jig	..	05	..	05
6. Remove drill from chuck	..	..	03	03
Totals	07	18	14	25

TIME, HUNDREDTHS OF A MINUTE

Motion and Time Study

NOTE: Add 0.15 min. when quick-change chuck is not used (cases B and C).

Add 0.06 min. for advancing work to next spindle.

Add 0.05 min. when reamer is oiled before entering hole.

12. *Use of formulas in setting standard time.* There are many examples in industry of the use of formulas in the calculation of a standard time. An excellent illustration is that of the work done at the Gleason Works of Rochester, New York, and reported by Lee and Vandevate.

For example, in setting rates for the cutting of straight spur gears by gear hubbers, the following formula applies, values being taken from tables covering such work:

Cutting Formula: $M = \dfrac{N \times L}{F \times S \times H}$

where M = cutting time in minutes.

N = number of teeth.

L = total length of cut (length of face + overtravel).

F = feed in inches per revolution of work.

S = speed of hob in rpm.

H = lead of hob; (a) single — 1; (b) double — 2.

13. *Ratio-delay study.* It is highly important in making time studies to determine the time lost by unavoidable interruptions, delays and variations in the performing of manufacturing operations. Since such delays vary in length and frequency, it is very difficult to measure them. The times when they may occur cannot be predicted. Analysis of the delays, however, may disclose conditions that are overlooked or unknown; yet which have a considerable effect upon output.

A special investigation in this field was made by Robert L. Morrow, the new method being called ratio-delay study. It is based upon a statistical technique which is highly practical, and produces results of a more closely accurate nature, and at less cost, than the extensive observations and recordings which had previously been used.

The first explorations in the field were conducted by L. H. C. Tippett in the English textile industry. He stated that if a large number of observations were taken at random intervals, recording whether or not a machine was in operation, "the percentage number of readings that record the machine as working will tend to equal the percentage time it is in that state."

When similar random readings are applied to an operator's cycle of work, "the percentage of readings recording the operatives as performing a certain operation or group of operations is an estimate of the percentage time spent in these operations." When such readings are "randomly distributed over a sufficiently long time, this relationship holds whether the machine stoppages or operations of the operatives are short or long, many or few, regular or irregular."

Motion and Time Study

In practice, each observation is made the instant the observer reaches a specified point, and notes whether the operator or machine is or is not working, and, if not, ascertains and records the cause. A summation of the times each cause of delay exists will indicate what steps to take to cut down or eliminate such occurrences.

14. *Fatigue.* Since fatigue is a factor in all work cycles, it is included in the factor for "personal, fatigue and delay allowances" in time studies. Rest periods are advisable in many kinds of work so that operators may recuperate almost completely at the time from the effects of fatigue. Higher average production is secured through definite rest periods, rather than by allowing for its slowing down under continuous operation.

Fatigue affects different people in different ways and will vary with the general nature of individuals in mental and physical makeup. The scientific data on the subject are meager, and much more study is necessary before methods to reduce fatigue and thus increase output can be developed.

15. *Motion economy.* Motion economy has as its aim the maximum output of a better product, at a lower cost, in the shortest possible time, achieved with the least expenditure of energy, and with the maximum well-being for the individual worker.

Frank B. Gilbreth, pioneering founder of this field of activity, rightfully said: "There is no waste of any kind in the world that equals the waste from needless, ill-directed, and ineffective motions, and the resulting unnecessary fatigue. Because this is true, there is no industrial opportunity that offers a richer return than the transformation of ill-directed and ineffective motion into efficient activity."

16. *Micromotion methods.* The work of Gilbreth and others has shown that motion study opens up opportunities for great time and cost savings. Even the skilled worker, who has learned his calling in the traditional manner, is often inefficient, and wastes much of his energy in useless motions.

Many motions of the workers on rapid work, however, are too quick to be caught by the human eye and segregated from connecting motions. To solve this problem, Gilbreth introduced the use of the motion picture camera to investigate such rapid motions. When this method is used, a clock of special design is placed near the workman whose motions are to be studied. This clock has a hand which makes 20 revolutions of the dial per minute, the dial being divided into 100 parts so that each division represents one two-thousandths of a minute.

A permanent record is thus obtained both of the operator's motions and the corresponding times. This picture can be studied in detail, and any unnecessary motions can be detected. At the same time, from the difference in clock readings at the beginning and end of a motion, the elapsed time can be obtained. Such a record is of great value in studying complex operations where the motions are many and rapid. Moreover, the film registers almost all the pertinent data, such as layout of the work place and arrangement of equipment. Thus, it provides a permanent record not only of the job but of all surrounding conditions.

Another interesting method used by Gilbreth was to fasten a small electric light bulb to the hand of the operator and connect it by flexible wiring to an intermittent source of current. The light in the surrounding area was then dimmed, and a photograph taken of the operator's movements by an ordinary camera. The diagram which was photographed on the plate in the form of flashes showed the path of the operator's hand. It was thus possible from this diagram to make deductions as to whether time could be saved by changing the method, or by correcting the workman's motions.

17. *Elements of motion or therbligs.* After years of research in this field, Frank Gilbreth and his wife, Dr. Lillian M. Gilbreth, succeeded in differentiating the fundamental motions used in performing an operation or cycle of work. Such elemental motions, for the want of a better name, were called "therbligs" (Gilbreth spelled backwards). They are identified by symbols, or industrial shorthand, as a short-cut in recording and reading.

In such studies, the motions of all parts of the body are accounted for. Since many of these are performed simultaneously, a chart known as a "simultaneous motion cycle chart" or "simo chart" was devised on which to show elapsed time, clock time, and the analysis of the cycle by the therblig method for each major part of the body that is called into action. From such studies, the Gilbreths evolved several laws of motion, of which the following are a condensation:

(a) Materials, tools, and equipment should be in the normal working area wherever possible. They should never be located outside the maximum working area.
(b) Motion of both hands and both arms should start and stop at the same time, and should be made in opposite directions through similar paths.
(c) Holding should not be done by the use of the hands. Use jigs and fixtures to do all the holding.
(d) Gravity feed bins for materials and drop-delivery should be used wherever practical.
(e) Materials, tools, and equipment should be prepositioned in definite locations, in relation to the order of operations and as close to the point of use as practical.

18. *Methods-Time-Measurement method.* Based on Gilbreth techniques and a study of many motion picture films of typical industrial operations, certain engineers have come forward with ways of setting predetermined times. Briefly, the procedure is to break a study down to its basic motions and apply certain predetermined standard times.

In the judgment of the author, the most practical of these methods is that known as M-T-M (Methods-Time-Measurement) devised by Harold B. Maynard and the Engineering Staff of Methods Engineering Council. Methods-Time-Measurement is a procedure which gives the actual relationship between basic motions and the time required to make them.

(a) It is based upon the fact that any manual operation is made up of distinct and recognizable basic motions.
(b) Each basic motion has a constant time value at the average performance level.
(c) Research, based upon the study of many industrial operations through motion picture films, has measured the time values for all basic motions. These time values are known as M-T-M data.

The unit of time used is the .00001 hour which is called a time measurement unit—abbreviated T.M.U. The tables show the number .00001 hours required by the operator of average skill, working with average effort to make the motion under average condition.

The scope of this textbook obviously does not permit a detailed discussion of this technique. The author, however, has seen this system installed in a number of plants in the United States, and has discussed it with engineers who have installed it in England, Sweden, Spain and other European countries. It is a very definite outgrowth of motion and time study, and probably will replace a lot of the activity in this field.

Review

What is meant by motion and time study?

Name the four fundamental purposes of motion and time study.

What factors must be considered in making motion and time studies?

Name and describe the two methods used in making motion and time studies.

Describe the procedure which a time-study man needs to follow.

What is meant by the leveling factor?

Describe the procedure followed in compiling instruction cards.

What is the purpose of motion economy?

What are therbligs?

What were some of the laws of motion evolved by the Gilbreths?

What is the Methods-Time-Measurement method?

CHAPTER XVI

Job Estimating

1. *Factors in a job estimate.* Job estimating is done for several important reasons which may be summarized as follows:

   (a) To estimate costs of producing or manufacturing lines of products which the company may wish to put on the market.
   (b) To set selling prices on the company's regular lines of products.
   (c) To estimate costs on special jobs which the company wishes to secure.
   (d) To ascertain the probable costs of undertaking certain available jobs in order to determine whether or not to submit bids for doing the work.
   (e) To recheck costs on the company's products to find out which products are profitable and selling in satisfactory volume, and which are not moving or are not profitable.
   (f) To solicit contracts from companies for doing specific kinds of manufacturing for which the company is particularly well equipped, and on which a good profit can be made.
   (g) To keep otherwise idle equipment at work to

pay its carrying costs and, if possible, to earn a profit on the work which it performs.

(h) To develop minimum cost figures at which jobs can be taken to keep the plant busy in periods of low manufacturing activity.

(i) To oblige certain good customers who are attempting to place some difficult work with an outside manufacturing company.

2. *Cost estimating.* Large plants manufacturing standard products of the company's own design have estimating departments which are organized to list the elements of costs in the various kinds of work performed, and to cut down these costs wherever possible along sound cost-reduction lines. The great volume of manufacturing carried on in highly competitive fields usually necessitates cost cutting, and consequently necessitates the design of products and parts for the most economical processing. Equipment design is followed by job estimating to find out what the probable unit cost of production will be.

In at least one very large mass-production organization, a system is in effect whereby costs can be worked out on an experimental basis. The manufacturing cost of a new part, or altered design of an existing part, continuously produced in large quantities, is calculated. A division within the organization may then contract to take over the manufacturing of this part at an agreed-upon unit price per piece for a certain period—the price being acceptable to the particular company.

Job Estimating

A proviso in the contract states that the contractor during this period may experimentally develop cost-reduction methods for producing the product, and retain all the profits realized from the savings in production. At the end of the stated period, the manufacture of the part reverts to the company, the procedure and layout developed by the contractor being integrated into the company's regular production lines. This system has proved to be a successful one, and is profitable to both company and contractor.

3. *Elements of a job estimate.* While there are wide variations in the details of job estimating, because of the innumerable varieties of products manufactured, there are common cost factors which enter into most estimates. These costs include the following thirteen important items:

(a) Labor costs.
(b) Supervision costs.
(c) Inspection costs.
(d) Materials costs.
(e) Use-of-equipment costs.
(f) Materials-handling costs.
(g) Plant overhead costs.
(h) Defective materials costs.
(i) Defective workmanship costs.
(j) Maintenance-of-equipment costs.
(k) Depreciation costs.
(l) Storage-of-materials costs.
(m) General overhead costs.

Labor costs are those for the direct operations carried on to produce the product. They are usually obtained daily through some form of production or time tickets from which the payroll is later made up and summarized. In some instances, bonuses are paid to workers for certain kinds of individual jobs, and these amounts are likewise obtained from the payroll.

Supervision costs are those incurred for foremen, assistant foremen, and group leaders who are concerned with directing or checking on the manufacturing operations. These costs are also obtainable from payroll records.

Inspection costs cover the checking or testing of materials used in producing the company's products, the checking of work-in-process in the manufacturing departments to see that it is within the standard tolerances, and the checking of finished products to release them to the finished-stock departments or the shipping department.

Materials costs are obtained from the stores-records department in the case of products produced from stocked materials, as well as in the case of parts and equipment which have been previously purchased and temporarily stored until needed for processing and assembly. Costs of special materials, parts and equipment which must be purchased from outside are obtained by asking for quotations from the various companies making such parts.

Use-of-equipment costs are those which may be cal-

Job Estimating

culated from manufacturing records showing when, and for how long, machines have been in productive operation over the current accounting period. This information will give data as to the average rates of use of machines. Cost records may show the current machine-hour rates charged for the use of the various kinds of machines. However, cost, age, physical condition, physical depreciation rate, relative obsolescence, present hourly rate of use, and current write-off rate must be frequently checked for all kinds of machinery and processing equipment in a manufacturing plant.

In this connection, consideration must be given to the fact that new and improved kinds of manufacturing equipment are constantly being developed. Individual machines are becoming available which perform a sequence of operations mechanically. Most important of all, automation, or the integration of several machines into production lines which mechanically perform sequences of operations without the attendance of an operator at all, is radically changing the situation. The advent of such equipment may necessitate extensive changes in equipment and layout in many manufacturing plants, particularly those engaged in mass production. Use-of-equipment costs, therefore, may undergo considerable changes, and may supplant the labor-cost factor in many cases.

Materials-handling costs for mobile equipment can be summarized and rated on the calculated time of use of the various kinds of motor trucks and hand or power-driven lift trucks in service in the plant. Since these services are carried on in considerable part by a separate transportation organization, their costs of operation can be fairly closely calculated from operators' time cards.

Distribution of the expense can be made according to the relative amount of time which these services devote to handling operations in the different departments. Costs for fixed systems serving individual departments can be calculated on the basis used for amortizing equipment of this kind. Costs for interdepartmental operating systems perhaps can be satisfactorily rated among the respective departments.

Plant-overhead costs usually include the many items which are not so specifically associated with the actual carrying on of operations, and therefore cannot be distributed among any class or classes of work. The items should be classified into whatever groups seem best to fit in with the operations of the individual plant. Cost accountants are usually able to develop acceptable methods for assigning these costs in a reasonable manner to the various operating or service divisions of the company.

Defective materials costs can usually be determined according to the cost value of the original material, including any reasonable storage charge, and any work done before the defectiveness of the material is discovered. In some cases, the defects cannot be noted until the materials are worked on. Where this limitation exists, agreements should be made with suppliers at the time of the purchases to take back the imperfect materials when their conditions are discovered.

Defective workmanship costs may be incurred where machines are out of adjustment, where the material is defective with the defect not readily apparent, or where the operator is not skilled or properly trained in his knowledge of materials. The company must accept the loss in most cases.

Maintenance-of-equipment costs are those for the upkeep and repair of manufacturing equipment. Since the equipment is located in different departments, these costs can usually be segregated and apportioned in proper ratio among the respective departments.

Depreciation costs are the amounts which should be written off annually in accordance with the age, condition and degree of obsolescence of the particular equipment, and its eventual retirement because of wear, decline in use, and inferiority to newer and modern equipment. Because of the continual advent of improved and automatically operated equipment, and of higher-production equipment of specialized kinds for particular kinds of operations conducted on a mass-production basis, it is often advisable to amortize numerous types of equipment within a quite limited period. In case the equipment does become obsolete, the plant is protected against the situation. In case the equipment is not superseded, it can be used longer, and the return on the investment is higher.

Storage-of-materials costs depend greatly upon whether the plant uses few materials or many materials; whether the materials are of high value or low value; whether they can be stored outdoors or must be kept indoors; and whether they are large in size and in volume carried, or small in size and amount carried. Such costs also depend on whether shipments of materials are frequent or infrequent; whether the materials are stable or subject to deterioration; and whether they can be readily sold if the products for which they have been used are no longer to be manufactured.

General overhead costs are such costs as those incurred in making repairs to plant or equipment. They also include insurance against fire, theft, and accidents to employees; public liability insurance; burglary insurance; pension funds for retired employees; reserves against contingencies; retirement of outstanding financial obligations.

4. *Procedures in job estimating.* A project is initiated either by a company's representative who calls upon a prospective client, or by an inquiry from some manufacturing company wishing to purchase certain equipment. The sales department, to which the proposal is referred, has its representative obtain any further information necessary from the prospective client, and then turns over to the plant's job-estimating department the following data:

(a) Information as to the prospective client's specific needs.

Job Estimating

(b) A statement as to the possibility of producing what is wanted.

(c) Opportunity to obtain the contract in competition with other companies.

(d) The time allowed for completing the work and making shipment.

(e) The possibility of developing further business along this line.

The job-estimating department then proceeds to draw up a proposal, including perhaps a preliminary set of sketches or drawings, an estimated cost, and a statement of probable delivery date, based on information obtained from the client by the sales representative or the sales department. If the contract is secured, further detailed information, if necessary, is obtained through the sales department, or, in cases of special equipment, by direct contact between client and manufacturer.

5. *Standards for job estimating.* Since the assembling, classification and calculating of data on manufacturing jobs is an expensive and time-consuming operation, it is advisable—except for very new and special jobs—to set up standard costs on all important operations which are, or may likely become, repetitive. Many of the detailed cost figures calculated on a job can be entered on the estimate sheets from the recorded standard costs. In this way, much time and cost in estimating can be saved, and the estimates can be more promptly developed and submitted. Furthermore, the skill attained in

making estimates is likely to result in the assembling of reliable data which can be of increasing use in future estimating.

It is not always necessary to be closely accurate in compiling cost data from previous classified records—except for highly competitive or standard kinds of work, or in cases where jobs are needed to keep the plant busy. Many infrequently manufactured products that are ordered are quite specialized, and therefore require a greater margin of possible profit to guard against possible loss in the transaction. A well-trained, capable staff of estimators will know when to bid closely. They will also know when it is necessary to increase the margin of safety in bidding because of special requirements in the proposed contract which may otherwise result in a loss instead of a profit on the job.

Review

Give some of the important reasons for doing job estimating.

What are the cost factors which enter into most job estimates?

Why may use-of-equipment costs undergo considerable changes in the future?

How can defective material costs be kept down?

Why is it advisable to amortize various types of equipment within a quite limited time?

Name some of the factors on which storage-of-materials costs depend.

What are included in general overhead costs?

Describe the procedure in job estimating.

CHAPTER XVII

Plant Maintenance

1. *Preventive maintenance.* Well-run modern plants no longer consider that plant maintenance is merely a matter of making repairs to buildings, machinery, service equipment, power plants, factory yard equipment, and other facilities, when breakdowns occur. Instead, the emphasis is initially centered on preventive maintenance. This means checking or inspecting plant facilities in order to adjust or repair them before failures occur, in case such facilities are found to be damaged, defective, or otherwise in need of attention. Lengthy shutdowns caused by neglect of maintenance work are exceedingly costly, and greatly disrupt manufacturing schedules.

2. *Difference between maintenance and repairs.* Frequently, little regard is given to the difference in meaning of the terms "maintenance" and "repair" in discussing work done on the plant and its equipment in order to keep them conditioned for service, and to prevent them from undergoing rapid deterioration. Nevertheless, it is well to distinguish clearly between these terms.

Strictly speaking, "maintenance" should be the term

used to designate the inspecting, cleaning, checking and adjusting of equipment, such as the regulating of service instruments and related equipment to keep them clean, accurate, serviceable, and reliable as operating, indicating or recording devices. The term "repairs" should be reserved for actual work done on buildings and equipment, such as replacing broken windows, repairing a damaged truck, installing new gears in a machine, welding a broken crankshaft, putting in new piping, and performing similar kinds of work on property or equipment.

3. *Maintenance department organization.* It is desirable to have plant maintenance work placed in charge of a plant maintenance engineer reporting to the plant manager, so that the engineer can have official authorization to take over any emergency assignment without the delay of securing special permission to make the necessary repairs. He should also operate under a financial budget, so that he can requisition and obtain materials, supplies, equipment and other facilities to carry on his work. In cases where costs of alterations, repairs and replacements are beyond standard limited allowance figures for such work, the plant maintenance engineer should be expected to submit a report and explanation of the situation to secure assent for proceeding with the work.

4. *Kinds of work done by the maintenance department.* Although the nature of maintenance work varies considerably among plants because of the wide difference

Plant Maintenance

in plant organization, the kinds of work generally done include the following:

(a) Building maintenance.
(b) Manufacturing equipment maintenance.
(c) Electrical equipment maintenance.
(d) Power plant maintenance.
(e) Heating, lighting, ventilating and plumbing equipment maintenance.
(f) Materials handling and transportation equipment maintenance.
(g) Service equipment facilities and maintenance.
(h) Painting maintenance.
(i) Management of maintenance equipment storeroom.
(j) Yard and grounds maintenance.
(k) Plant and yard equipment retirement and disposal.

5. *Building maintenance.* In a large plant, especially one having numerous buildings, building maintenance is a major responsibility. Consequently, a separate construction unit may have to be set up to do all the work required in maintaining existing buildings, making alterations in buildings, constructing additions to buildings, and even erecting new buildings. A considerable part of building-maintenance work is confined to certain items.

For example, particular attention needs to be given to factory floors, which are usually made of concrete. Factory floors carry the weight of equipment, and when heavy machines are to be installed, it is important to check on the allowable floor load, as well as on the amount of jarring or vibration of the floor when the equipment is in operation. Sometimes, very heavy equipment, such as presses, may require heavy foundations, which occasionally may even have to be separated from the floor of the factory. The floors should be surfaced with hard, durable material for long life and easy cleaning.

In addition to floors, interior doors in the factory require considerable attention. These doors should be hung to swing in both directions, if possible, for convenience when industrial trucks are used for plant transportation. Wire glass can be put in the door panels for avoiding accidents which might otherwise occur as the result of workers or trucks approaching the door blindly at the same time from opposite sides. The doors should be surfaced with heavy metal plates so that trucks can bump the doors open as they pass through. The doors should be inspected at frequent intervals to detect and replace damaged plates.

Continuous attention must also be given to traffic aisles which should be kept marked off by durable paint. No material or equipment should be placed or piled in the aisles except in an emergency. Another steady maintenance job is that of taking care of toilets and washrooms. These should be inspected and thoroughly cleaned daily, and kept supplied with such items as soap and towels.

Plant Maintenance

6. *Manufacturing equipment maintenance.* Machines —especially those engaged in high-precision work—require frequent adjustment and repair. Either the machinist or the inspector keeps a check on the parts produced, and calls for an adjustment or tool change when an operator's machine turns out work just at tolerance limits.

The adjustment and set-up of machines are often done by an expert machinist who is assigned to do such work, especially in cases where machines are run by machine operatives who are not skilled mechanics. This machinist sets up the machine and runs through a trial piece, if necessary, to make sure that the piece is within the set tolerances at all important dimensions. He then releases the machine for production.

7. *Maintenance of electrical equipment.* Electrical-equipment maintenance is very important because much of the machinery in operation in a plant is run by electric motors. These must be continually inspected and kept in repair to prevent the disruption of operations. In most instances, plants have replacement motors available for practically all of the operating equipment, so that defective motors can be taken to the electrical shop and repaired, and later restored to service.

8. *Power plant maintenance.* In the maintenance of power plants, boilers have to be cleaned after a certain period of use, and scale must be removed. Steam turbines, generators and motors require lubrication and adjustment. Pump bearings have to be repacked, and

gaskets in pipelines must be replaced, while changes in wiring are necessary when equipment is to be installed or moved.

9. *Lighting maintenance.* Industrial plants which have electric generating equipment may operate their own alternating current lighting systems which require maintenance work. Usually, they have a tie-in with public utility plants in case of power failures of their own equipment.

10. *Heating, ventilating and plumbing maintenance.* Heating systems—boilers, pipelines, radiators and return lines—require changes from time to time, and must undergo frequent inspection and adjustment. Boilers must be blown down and cleaned of scale and sediment, flange pipe joints occasionally need repacking or new gaskets, unions have to be tightened, and radiator valves require repacking. Ventilating fans and ducts need cleaning, and the fans require oiling. Plumbing systems must be inspected at regular intervals to prevent leaks from developing and to keep the systems in otherwise good order.

11. *Materials-handling and transportation equipment maintenance.* Materials-handling equipment usually undergoes severe service and needs periodic maintenance. Mobile equipment, such as motor trucks, common industrial hand trucks, hand-lift trucks, industrial power-driven trucks, tractor-trailer equipment, motorized "walkies," electric and gasoline fork-lift trucks, elevators, hoists, jib cranes, floor cranes, overhead

Plant Maintenance

traveling cranes and gantry cranes, have revolutionized materials handling in factory plants and yards, and have vastly reduced costs of practically every kind of handling. All such equipment must undergo frequent inspection to keep it in good shape.

A majority of plants perform their own maintenance work on materials-handling equipment and carry stocks of parts for this purpose. Maintenance on trucks includes keeping batteries charged, oiling or greasing operating mechanisms, replacing tires, and replacing worn or broken parts.

12. *Service-installations maintenance.* Service installations are of great importance to a plant. Such installations include alarm systems, plant and outside telephone facilities, in-plant call systems, two-way radio communications systems, first-aid and plant hospital facilities, plant lunchrooms and restrooms. Alarm and communications systems for immediate outside and inside calls save a large amount of time, and may prevent heavy losses in sudden emergencies. These services must be checked daily and adjusted or repaired at once if they are out of order.

13. *Painting-maintenance work.* Painting-maintenance work can be profitably carried on by following a regular schedule that is based on a planned program of redecorating. Most plants which have been erected in recent years are of brick or concrete. Consequently, so far as the exterior goes, it is usually necessary to paint only window frames and outside doors.

Plant offices, hallways, stairways, reception rooms and other areas need to be kept well-painted or decorated, partly because those who have business with the company usually visit the office region. In many cases, factory departments have to be painted less frequently. If, however, the company is engaged in manufacturing such products as foods, beverages, confectionery, medicines or surgical accessories, the manufacturing areas must be kept in the best of sanitary condition.

14. *Plant-yard maintenance.* If the plant has considerable yard storage—especially of valuable materials—it is advisable to fence in the property, preferably by metal fencing, and to keep gates closed except for truck entrance and exit. Barbed wire along the top will stop most trespassing. Entrances should be kept clear, and the yard should be kept neat for the purpose of making a favorable impression and creating public good will.

Plant yards and grounds require certain maintenance work to keep them cleared of discarded items, broken machinery, defective or spoiled materials of only scrap value, old lumber, and factory wastes. A particular location in a little-used section of the plant yard may be used for temporary storage of such refuse. As soon as an appreciable amount has accumulated, however, it should be sold to dealers, or burned if inflammable, or trucked to an out-of-town dump if no other place of disposal is available.

When a plant is located on a highway, a well-traveled street, or in a residential or semi-residential

Plant Maintenance

area, good public relations dictates that the buildings and grounds be attractively laid out, well-kept, orderly, properly landscaped, and in all respects a credit to the community.

15. *Maintenance service.* In a well-run plant, maintenance service is set up under a system whereby all calls for adjustments or repairs are classified for handling. Emergency jobs must be taken care of immediately. Other jobs can wait a reasonable amount of time before they are done.

The maintenance department usually has so much work to do that it is practically always kept busy. Many plants find it necessary to keep a day shift available for both emergency and routine work up to the limits of the capacity of the maintenance department. Usually, a night crew is also needed to take care of repairs which must be done after the plant closes for the day. Jobs requiring more time than is available before the next day may have to be postponed to be done over the week-end. A few plants may have annual shutdowns for the vacation period. During such a time, the plant maintenance crew takes over, and does the major portion of any required repair work.

16. *Maintenance-equipment-and-supplies storeroom.* So far as reasonably possible, it is advisable to have all maintenance equipment and supplies carried in a maintenance storeroom, fairly centrally located, and convenient to the headquarters of the maintenance division itself. Except in a small plant, it is advisable to place

the maintenance storeroom under the control of a storeskeeper, as is done in the case of raw materials and supplies to be made into finished products.

The maintenance storeskeeper should require a stores-issue slip for the items which a maintenance man needs, and this slip should be signed by the requisitioner. When various returnable items of equipment or supplies are brought back to the maintenance storeroom, the storeroom clerk should give the workman a receipt for the returned items. In this way, the maintenance storeroom records and the materials physically on hand can be kept in approximate agreement.

17. *Maintenance records.* Practically all manufacturing plants keep maintenance records. These records serve the important purpose of controlling maintenance work. They are kept in folders, or loose-leaf binders, or on maintenance-record cards. There should be a folder or card for each of the items of maintenance equipment listed previously in this chapter. Among the advantages of such a system are the following:

(a) Each important item of equipment is recorded, with the date of its acquirement and installation entered. The age of the equipment is thus known.

(b) All maintenance work done on the equipment is entered, and a service record is thus set up. As a result, the person in charge of plant equipment can find out at any time how much it has cost the company to keep the particular equip-

Plant Maintenance

ment in satisfactory service. Equipment which has not come up to expectations can thus be marked for disposal.

(c) The cost of the equipment is on record, and the performance of the equipment can be checked against other equipment of a competitive nature whenever the company decides to purchase additional new equipment of a similar nature.

(d) If the company has an amortization program for the writing off of equipment, the estimated current value of the equipment may be ascertained at any time. This will provide a guide as to whether to dispose of the equipment or return it in service. In case of sale, the company has a means for evaluating the current worth of the equipment to the company, and the price at which it should be sold to a buyer.

(e) The equipment records set up make it possible to take a plant-equipment inventory in a short time and with the least trouble.

Review

What is meant by "preventive maintenance"?

How does the term "maintenance" differ in meaning from the term "repair"?

How should a maintenance department be organized?

Name some of the kinds of work done by plant-maintenance departments.

What are some of the items which require particular attention in building maintenance?

Describe a method for assuring proper maintenance of manufacturing equipment.

Give examples of materials-handling and transportation equipment, and state why it must be frequently inspected.

How is good maintenance service provided?

What needs to be done to assure the proper functioning of the maintenance-equipment-and-supplies storeroom?

State the advantages of keeping maintenance records.

CHAPTER XVIII

Wage Control and Salary Incentive Systems

1. *Wage payment plans.* All successful wage payment plans are based upon two fundamental principles. One principle is that the general wage level established in the plant should be at least equal to the going wage level for comparable work in the community. The other principle is that the wage rate for each job or operation should be established in relation to the wage rates for other jobs in the plant, with due regard for differences in skill, effort, responsibility, and working conditions.

Workers left to their own initiative, in general, do not produce anywhere near to full capacity. The old method was to obtain production through a driving, domineering foreman. While the studies of Frederick W. Taylor and his successors showed that much loafing on the job was an inherent difficulty, they also showed that the average worker possessed no information concerning the maximum capacities of machine tools and processes. Further investigation proved that, even when the worker was instructed by scientific methods in the most efficient use of his tools, his interest in increased production had to be stimulated.

To get the maximum output from average machine-shop workers, Taylor found that it was necessary to pay 30 per cent more that the average basic rate. This extra compensation was of an incentive nature. In computing it, use was made of a variety of wage or incentive systems of rewarding labor. Compensation under incentive systems should not be confused with basic wages. Such systems are merely mechanisms through which the management holds out incentives to encourage higher production.

2. *Essentials of a good wage payment plan.* An incentive plan is not a cure-all. It can be effective only with proper organization, layout, production control, and job standardization. As Charles W. Lytle so aptly points out in "Wage Incentive Methods": "Incentive plans are like oats for a horse; oats cannot change the breed but can maintain the spirit."

To be successful, a wage payment plan should have nine characteristics, according to Lytle. Specifically, such a plan should be:

(a) Just to both employer and employee.
(b) Strong in task and reward for high productivity.
(c) Unrestricted as to amount of earnings; rate should be guaranteed against change until job is changed.
(d) Easy to calculate; prompt and clear in relation to individual performance.
(e) Flexible and intimately related to other management controls.

Wage Control and Salary Incentive Systems

(f) An aid to teamwork, i.e., automatically assist supervision.

(g) Supported by employees, i.e., be in no respect paternalistic.

(h) Supported to fullest extent by management in matter of products, materials and quality control, maintenance of equipment, etc.

(i) Kept in continual use, i.e., should not be used temporarily in busy seasons and dropped in bad times to reduce wages.

To the foregoing list should be added the following requirements, pointed out by Joseph A. Piacitelli, if a wage payment plan is to be successful:

(a) The wage rate should be guaranteed to assure workers their basic wages in the event that unusual operating conditions, not within their control, lower their productivity.

(b) The wage rate should be designed and based on units of measure capable of being used with other management controls.

Generally speaking, a wage plan should be developed to meet a specific need. The type of plan devised should depend upon such factors as the nature of the work, type of labor, length of runs, and kind of work handled.

3. *Fundamental systems of wage payment.* There are only two fundamental methods of rewarding the worker. The first one is to pay him for the amount of *time* that he spends on his work. The second is to pay

him for the amount of work he performs. Paying for the amount of time put in on a job is usually characterized as *day-work* because the worker is paid a certain rate per hour, or a certain rate per day. Paying for the amount of work produced is usually called *piecework* because the compensation is by the job, or by the piece. All wage systems are founded on these two fundamentals. They may clearly fall into either of the two classifications, or may be a combination of both.

4. *Day-wage plan.* The day-wage method of rewarding labor is without doubt the oldest plan. To illustrate this plan, let it be assumed that a worker is to receive pay at the rate of $.50 per hour. He works on the basis of an eight-hour day. His pay is computed at 8 × $.50, or $4.00 per day. This simple relationship may be expressed as the time worked, T, times the rate per hour, R, equal to TR. TR, then, equals earnings, E, and a simple expression has been developed which may be written:

$$E = TR$$

One advantage of the day-wage plan is that the worker is guaranteed a certain amount of pay per day. This assured amount eliminates uncertainties that have developed under straight piecework and certain bonus plans that do not guarantee a certain minimum amount. A second advantage of this plan is that the payroll is easy to calculate. This feature is a boon to time clerks and payroll clerks. A third advantage is that the company is enabled to reward older and more experienced

Wage Control and Salary Incentive Systems

employees for service or efficiency by giving them a higher day-wage. Such a plan is impossible under straight piece-rate.

A disadvantage of the day-wage plan is that there is no incentive encouraging the worker to increase production. This lack is the main disadvantage, and it has caused the replacement of day-work in many plants by some form of incentive plan.

5. *Piecework systems—old method.* The fundamental feature of piecework systems is that the worker is paid in direct proportion to the amount he produces. Such a plan operates as follows:

If the rate per piece is $.10 and the production 80 pieces per day, the worker's pay per day will be $.10 × 80 = $8.00. Algebraically, this may be expressed as the number of pieces, N, times the rate per piece, r; equal earnings, E, or as follows:

$$E = Nr$$

If many pieces of a different character are handled daily, piecework is very difficult to apply. It finds its greatest adaptability in repetitive work, where a large number or parts are the same. Under certain conditions, it may be applied to a small number of parts, particularly if the parts are large and a close estimate can be made as to the time required.

6. *Difficulties encountered under the old piece-rate system.* The great difficulty with the old piece-rate system was the fact that the price per piece was set by the *guess* of the foreman or the supervisor. In former days,

a knowledge of scientific principles did not exist, and the records that did exist were unreliable for setting standards. When the rate established by guess was first released to the shop, the workers usually speeded up and boosted their wages far beyond the expectancy of the management. As a result, there was a cut in wages; that is, the price per piece was reduced.

It often happened, however, that labor was still able to boost production and earn a high figure. If it did, another cut in rates was likely. After a couple of such wage cuts in piecework, the worker, in disgust, set a certain limit on his output and refused to go beyond it. Thus was brought about the limiting of production, in spite of the piecework system, due entirely to the lack of knowledge of the management as to how many pieces should constitute a day's work. Taylor solved the problem by the introduction of the modern scientific job analysis and time-study methods of determining correct output and wage rates.

7. *Objections to piecework.* Objections of another nature also caused difficulty with the old piecework system. In day-work, no rush was involved in getting a day's wage. Hence, a great many workers preferred the day-work plan. Under piecework, an employee might earn considerably more that the ordinary day-wage, but if he encountered machine trouble or hard castings, the loss thus incurred was entirely his own. Another difficulty was that labor unions opposed piecework on the ground that it encouraged unrestricted individual

Wage Control and Salary Incentive Systems

competition. Furthermore, the worker, resenting successive cuts in piece-rates, and prone to object to any method that called for greater output on his part without additional reward, took steps to make the plan lose its effectiveness.

The advantages which the old piecework system had may be summed up as follows:

(a) There was an incentive to maximum production.
(b) An appeal was made individually to a great many workers.
(c) The amount of pay was easily computed both by the worker and the payroll clerk.
(d) The worker was paid in exact proportion to his output.

The following were disadvantages of the old piecework system:

(a) There was no provision in such a plan for rewarding anything but quantity. The usual practice in regard to quality was to pay only for good pieces.
(b) The absence of a minimum rate per day in case of machine breakdowns, smaller volume of work because of a falling off of orders, and other causes beyond the worker's control, made it unfair to him and hard to introduce.

8. *Modern wage systems.* To overcome the difficulties brought up by the old piece-work system, various wage

plans have been devised. Among the best-known plans may be included (1) the Halsey premium plan; (2) the Rowan plan; (3) the Taylor differential piece-rate plan; (4) the Gantt task and bonus plan; (5) the Emerson efficiency plan; (6) the standard hour, or 100 per cent premium plan; (7) the measured day-work plan; (8) the Bedaux Point System; (9) the group system plan; and (10) the combined piece-rate and hourly guarantee, or modern piece-rate plan.

9. *Combined piece-rate and hourly guarantee, or modern piece-rate plan.* Under the modern piece-rate plan, the disadvantages of other plans are largely eliminated, and this plan stands as one of the best methods of rewarding labor on an incentive basis. There are probably more plants operating under this piece-rate plan than under any other incentive system. This plan is superior to other methods, particularly to the older methods, because of the following:

(a) Standards are carefully set by time study and a study of the worker.
(b) There has been introduced the guaranteed minimum day-rate, which plays such a prominent part in all modern systems.

The modern piece-rate plan is expressed mathematically as follows:

$$E = TR + (N - N_s) r$$

In this equation, T = time taken, R = guaranteed rate per hour, N = total number of pieces, N_s = standard number of pieces that should be produced in the given period, and r = rate per piece for work above standard output. E = TR as a guaranteed minimum.

10. *Quality bonus.* The wage payment methods previously discussed are based on quantity, leaving the quality factor up to the inspection department. The worker receives pay for only those pieces that pass inspection. Under mass-production methods, inspection must be administered with increasing vigilance. Rigidly-enforced inspection penalizes the worker for poor product. It is possible, however, to give consideration to quality in bonus payments, and certain companies have evolved plans whereby the worker is paid an extra financial reward for high quality of product.

11. *Waste-elimination bonus.* Conservation in the use of materials and supplies is brought about by awarding bonuses for savings made by lowering previous consumption rates of such items in producing the same volumes of manufactured goods. In the cutting of such materials as fabrics, sheet stock, lumber and hides, and in the use of oil, chemicals and other supplies, workers often are wasteful because they do not know the costs of such items and the total amounts annually lost. When workers are informed of the values, and offered bonuses for reductions in consumption, they acquire a personal interest in conservation because they are given the opportunity to share in the resulting savings.

12. *Other wage plans tried by companies.* A number of representative companies have experimented with

the cost-of-living index as a means of raising or lowering wages. Under this plan, the base rates of pay are raised or lowered at definite periods in accordance with the change in the cost-of-living index. In some cases, changes in wage rates in the different areas where a company has plants may depend on changes in living costs in each particular area, rather than on changes in the national average.

Improved profit-sharing methods have been devised. One company adopted a monthly bonus plan based upon the company's net income for the previous three consecutive months. Under such plans, the whole organization is keyed up to get out orders and meet deliveries. The difficulty is that the addition to workers' incomes is small when business is dull, and falls to nothing in bad times. In most cases, workers apparently prefer regular wage plans with incentives rather than profit-sharing methods.

13. *Annual wage plans.* In certain industries, annual wage plans have had successful application. While such plans have been in effect for a long time in the case of clerical workers, professional staff personnel, executives, and others in the more stabilized occupations, it has been only in recent years that they have been used among wage earners in industries. Annual wage plans are growing in demand by wage earners as one of the elements in greater job security. In some cases, such plans are also favored by management, especially in seasonal industries, such as canning and meat packing,

Wage Control and Salary Incentive Systems

where there is need for overtime in busy seasons and layoffs in slack periods.

Annual wage plans are advantageous in that they do the following:

(a) Provide regular weekly or monthly pay, usually of a stated amount, the year round, thus leveling off family incomes and budgets over the annual period.
(b) Give a basis for holiday and vacation pay without special provisions.
(c) Tend to stabilize employment and prevent layoffs by causing companies to do more preplanning.
(d) Help seasonal industries by allowing them to pay straight wages for more than normal hours in peak periods, provided that in conformity with the Wage-Hour Act, these industries guarantee 1,000 hours of work for a 6-months' period, or 2,000 hours of work for a year's period, and do not in any case exceed 12 hours per day or 56 hours per week.

Annual wage plans are most readily applied in consumer goods industries, such as food and clothing, where there is not likely to be wide fluctuations in the demand for the product, particularly in periods of general business depression. Such plans present a serious problem, however, to basic industries in durable goods lines, such as those producing raw or partly fabricated materials, machine tools, or railroad equipment. These industries cannot easily adopt annual wage plans because their customers are largely other manufacturers whose demands may drop off over 80 per cent during a depression. There are times, therefore, when the sales income of the basic industries declines to such an extent that they are left with no funds available to carry along annual wage guarantees.

14. *Financial incentive for supervisors and executives.* Since supervisors and executives are not engaged directly in productive work where output or physical conservation can be the measure of awards, there is no direct way of offering them inducements for superior performance of duties over and above the requirements for holding their respective positions. Salary increases may not always compensate, or offer sufficient incentive, for making the extra effort.

For the supervisory staff, an incentive plan based upon savings in operating cost is often found highly effective. Improvements in work methods, application of labor-saving equipment, conservation in materials, and reductions in overhead expenses can be brought about most readily by such men who are in direct charge of operations. It is easy to set up reasonable budget plans as a basis for calculating and paying for any savings. The awards may be paid on a monthly or quarterly basis, after the economies have been measured, with an extra annual award for especially noteworthy performance.

Plans based upon annual profits can be applied to

Wage Control and Salary Incentive Systems

higher executives. In some cases, such profit-sharing plans provide the major portion of the annual compensation. These plans are often necessary to obtain the most capable men to head the enterprise, and to assure high salary and wage scales for the supervisory and working forces. Such plans, however, are likely to be attacked by workers and the unions as providing the executives with the means to further their own fortunes at the expense of the rank and file of the organization.

15. *Trends in industrial wage payments.* Legislation in recent years has affected the administration of wage payment plans. Among the changes brought about are the following:

(a) Basic wage rates and hours are regulated by law.
(b) Collective bargaining has become mandatory where workers demanded it.
(c) Company unions have been declared illegal.
(d) New vertical unions (C.I.O.) have formed the basis for united action by the workers in specific industries.
(e) Job rating for jobs and merit rating for workers have received wide attention.
(f) The whole concept of industrial relations has changed.

Many unions have accepted modern forms of piece-rate wage plans. Bargaining is carried out merely on the relative wage rates and job standards. In some set-ups, all piece rates must be approved by the unions. On the other hand, some union officials are antagonistic to the incentive form of wage payment. This is especially true during membership drives when many substandard workers may be drawn into the union ranks because of the possibility of wage increases.

Recent tendencies on the part of unions have been toward bargaining for flat rate increases even in industries where incentive plans are in effect. The incentive portion of the pay thus tends to be made relatively less of an inducement to productive effort. This situation has characterized the textile industry in certain large areas. Plant managers regard incentives as gradually losing their stimulus when they begin to fall below 30 per cent of the regular wage rates for jobs.

16. *Success of incentive systems rests with management.* When incentive systems have failed, the cause of such failures, according to Joseph A. Piacitelli, can usually be traced to one or more of the following management weaknesses:

- (a) Policy governing wage incentives not clear.
- (b) Improper method of setting standards.
- (c) Inadequate methods work.
- (d) Lack of uniform technique and policy governing the establishment of standards.
- (e) Inadequate records of methods.
- (f) Insufficient instruction to employees on methods of work.
- (g) Lack of participation by supervisors in the development of incentive systems.

Wage Control and Salary Incentive Systems

(h) Failure to enlist the cooperation of employees.
(i) Failure to guarantee standards.
(j) Lack of interest in employees' failure to attain standards.
(k) Incentive system not supported by other management controls.

Piacitelli suggests the following check list for testing the effectiveness of any wage incentive plan:

(a) Have you made clear your policy on wage incentives to all concerned?
(b) Is the plan designed to be fair to both management and labor?
(c) Is it easily understood by all employees affected by it?
(d) Does it guarantee standards against change?
(e) Does it guarantee basic wages established through job evaluation or otherwise?
(f) Does the plan tie in with other phases of management, such as planning, scheduling and control of quality?
(g) Are standards of performance determined by proper management engineering practice?
(h) Are the methods of work the best that can be devised?
(i) Do you have a clear-cut statement of policy governing methods of determining standards?
(j) Have you adequate records of the methods upon which rates are based?
(k) Are you giving employees sufficient instructions to assure attainment of standards?

(l) Are you making every effort to understand causes of workers' failure to attain standard, and doing something about them?

(m) Have you gained the confidence of your employees?

(n) Are your supervisors fully cooperative and do they have sufficient understanding of all phases of this problem to be able to answer the employees' questions?

Review

State the two fundamental principles on which all successful wage payment plans are based.

Name some of the essentials of a good wage payment plan.

What are the two fundamental methods of rewarding the worker?

State the advantages and disadvantages of the day-wage plan.

What difficulties were encountered under the old piece-rate system?

State the modern piece-rate plan in mathematical terms and explain.

State the advantages of annual wage plans, and explain why such plans cannot be readily adopted by some companies.

How has the administration of wage payment plans been affected by legislation in recent years?

As a means of testing the effectiveness of a wage incentive plan, what are some of the questions which should be asked?

CHAPTER XIX

Job Evaluation

1. *Nature and purpose.* Job evaluation is the device for analyzing tasks which, in the main, have repetitive cycles, so that standard methods of procedure may be established for the tasks, standard amounts of work output may be set, and wage rates may be finally fixed that are equitable in relation to other similar standardized tasks in the company and in the local area.

The setting of the wage rates themselves is a function separate from job evaluation as such. The money wages offered and paid in different localities for the same kinds of jobs may vary considerably in amount, in accordance with the cost of living, strength of local labor organizations, and other modifying factors in the particular industrial or business area under consideration.

2. *Setting up wage and salary plans.* In setting up wage and salary plans, it is important first to develop a complete program, and then work out each step in conformity with the over-all plan. The necessary steps are as follows:

  (a) Acquainting those who are to do the rating with the successful basic plans already in use, so that they may obtain a sound working knowledge of the subject.

(b) Selecting the general plan which seems most suitable from among the many varieties of plans available.

(c) Informing employees about the proposed plan.

(d) Formulating and adapting a specific detailed description of each particular job which is done in the company.

(e) Evaluating each job according to its relative degree and importance under the plan.

(f) Assigning proper titles to each job.

(g) Assembling information from other companies in the locality, or throughout the industry, as to their relative wage rates, so as to set up equivalent rates for corresponding types of jobs.

(h) Setting up wage and salary scales in conformity with local rates throughout the community, and particularly in line with the range of responsibility, the difficulty of performance and any objectionable features of each specific kind of job performed in the company.

(i) Providing for modifications or extensions to the plan in case changes may occur in jobs, or new jobs may be set up in the plant.

(j) Formulating wage-administration policies and procedures to administer the plan successfully, and keep it in full effect according to future developments.

(k) Keeping the plan up-to-date in conformity with developments throughout local industries and

Job Evaluation

in line with trends in the community itself, with regard to any future dealings with unions, collective bargaining with employees, and changes in federal, state or local laws.

3. *Determination of relative value of jobs.* Job rating has been defined as the means for analyzing a job in terms of the degree of skill, effort, responsibility and working conditions as they are related to the other jobs performed in the individual company. Job requirements are analyzed in detail to form the basis for establishing the wage rates to be paid for the various kinds of occupations in the particular plant.

4. *General types of job measurement.* Three general types of job measurement are in use for evaluating jobs in any kind of organization. These are job ranking, factor comparison and factor point scoring. Job ranking is actually not a process of evaluation, but rather a plan for evaluating the relative jobs in a company on the basis of estimated difficulty and relative worth.

Job classification is sometimes called a fourth method. This method, however, corresponds closely with job ranking, except that over-all classes of work are first set, and then jobs are ranked within these classes. Factor comparison and factor point scoring are the only complete methods, since they evaluate the elements of jobs in a thorough and organized manner.

5. *Job ranking plan.* Under the job ranking plan, there is a measurement of jobs by over-all comparison. A committee of shop personnel usually does the rating.

Table 2 shows a typical list of certain jobs in a plant, and the points values and ranking set on these jobs, respectively, by the individual members of the appointed job ranking committee:

Table 2

METHOD OF RATING BY THE JOB RANKING SYSTEM

TYPE OF JOB	Shop Supt.	Tool Room Supt.	Mach. Shop Supt.	Employment Mgr.	Job Analyst	Total Scores	Job * Rank
A— Simple Bench Assembly	1	2	2	2	1	8	2
B— Common Laborer	2	1	1	1	2	7	1
C— Metal Plater—1st Class	3	3	3	3	3	15	3
D— Machinist—1st Class	5	4	5	4	4	22	4
E— Toolmaker—1st Class	4	5	4	5	5	23	5

* 1 equals lowest and 5 equals highest rank of value

6. *Factor comparison system.* The factor comparison system is based on the premise that certain factors are common to all jobs. Components rated are mentality, skill, responsibility, mental application, physical application, and working conditions. Each of these factors is defined. The procedure is then as follows:

(a) Typical key jobs are selected and rated by each member of the committee in terms of the separate factors as shown in Table 3.

Job Evaluation

(b) When these ratings have been made by the individual members, they are combined, and average ratings for the key jobs are set up, as in Table 4.

(c) Next, according to job factors, the current rate of pay for each key job is set according to the average rankings developed in Table 5.

(d) Finally, the rates in Table 5 are compared with the hourly rates paid throughout the manufacturing area in which the company is located, and adjustments are made so as to conform to such area wage scales.

Table 3

RATING OF KEY JOBS

KEY JOBS	MENTAL-ITY	SKILL	RESPON-SIBILITY	MENTAL APPLICA-TION	PHYSICAL APPLICA-TION	WORKING CONDI-TIONS
Simple Bench Assembly	2	2	1	2	3	1
Common Laborer	1	1	2	1	5	4
Metal Plater—1st Class	3	3	3	3	4	5
Machinist—1st Class	4	4	4	4	2	3
Toolmaker—1st Class	5	5	5	5	1	2

7. *Factor point scoring system.* The factor point scoring system goes further than the factor comparison system on the basis that some jobs are more important than others and require varying weights and values for

Table 4

AVERAGE OF ALL COMMITTEE MEMBERS' RANKING OF KEY JOBS

KEY JOBS	MENTAL-ITY	SKILL	RESPON-SIBILITY	MENTAL APPLICA-TION	PHYSICAL APPLICA-TION	WORKING CONDI-TIONS
Simple Bench Assembly	2.1	2.3	1.3	1.8	1.2	1.8
Common Laborer	1.3	1.6	1.5	1.1	4.6	4.3
Metal Plater—1st Class	2.9	3.1	3.4	2.3	3.2	4.5
Machinist—1st Class	4.1	3.9	4.3	3.5	2.4	3.6
Toolmaker—1st Class	4.4	4.2	4.6	3.9	2.2	3.3

Table 5

OVER-ALL COMMITTEE ESTIMATES OF ALLOCATION OF PRESENT HOURLY RATES

KEY JOBS	MENTAL-ITY	SKILL	RESPON-SIBILITY	MENTAL APPLICA-TION	PHYSICAL APPLICA-TION	WORKING CONDI-TIONS
Simple Bench Assembly	.13	.15	.09	.10	.07	.65
Common Laborer	.07	.90	.08	.06	.25	.78
Metal Plater—1st Class	.15	.17	.18	.12	.18	1.05
Machinist—1st Class	.26	.25	.28	.22	.16	1.40
Toolmaker—1st Class	.33	.31	.34	.28	.10	1.60

the individual job factors. It also provides for a more positive rating means by using degrees, say 3 to 5, for each job factor, as in Table 6.

Job Evaluation

Job factors and degrees are specifically defined. The process of evaluation is by measuring job requirements in terms of the job factor and factor degree of definitions. The analyst must constantly refer back to the definitions, thus making the system more consistent throughout. The evaluations are supplemented through comparisons of the scores given to jobs previously rated.

Table 6

JOB FACTOR POINT SCORING PLAN

JOB FACTOR	1ST DEGREE	2ND DEGREE	3RD DEGREE	4TH DEGREE	5TH DEGREE
Skill					
1. Education	14	28	42	56	70
2. Experience	22	44	66	88	110
3. Initiative and Ingenuity	14	28	42	56	70
Effort					
4. Physical Demand	10	20	30	40	50
5. Mental or Visual Demand	5	10	15	20	25
Responsibility					
6. Equipment or Process	5	10	15	20	25
7. Material or Product	5	10	15	20	25
8. Safety of Others	5	10	15	20	25
9. Work of Others	5	10	15	20	25
Job Conditions					
10. Working Conditions	10	20	30	40	50
11. Hazards	5	10	15	20	25

Grade	Score Range	Grade	Score Range
12	Up to 139	6	250–271
11	140–161	5	272–293
10	162–183	4	294–315
9	184–205	3	316–337
8	206–227	2	338–359
7	228–249	1	360–381

Table 7 shows how the grades or degrees for a specific factor are identified, defined and evaluated. The purpose is to measure the job requirements in terms of the mental development needed to understand and think along the lines of the work to be performed. This mental development, or technical knowledge, may be acquired by either formal schooling or equivalent experience, trades training, or vocational training.

Table 7

TYPICAL LIST OF REQUIREMENTS IN EDUCATION AND MENTAL DEVELOPMENT

1st Degree

Requires the ability to read and write, add and subtract whole numbers.

2nd Degree

Requires the use of simple arithmetic such as addition and subtraction of decimals and fractions; together with simple drawings and some measuring instruments such as caliper, scale.

3rd Degree

Requires the use of fairly complicated drawings, advanced shop mathematics, handbook formulas, variety of precision measuring instruments, some trade knowledge in a specialized field or process.

4th Degree

Requires the use of complicated drawings and specifications, advanced shop mathematics, wide variety of precision measuring instruments, broad shop trade knowledge.

5th Degree

Requires a basic technical knowledge sufficient to deal with complicated and involved mechanical, electrical or other engineering problems.

8. *Classes of work to be covered.* The basic principles of job evaluation employed in factory work apply also

Job Evaluation

in office, supervisory and professional work. If, however, more than one of those classes of work are to undergo job evaluation, it will be necessary to vary to some extent the following: (1) the factors to be taken into account, (2) the procedures to follow in evaluating the different kinds of work, and (3) the modifications in standards which must be introduced to accomplish the necessary results in each major class. The divisions into which work may be subdivided are given in Table 8.

In most cases, the different kinds of work have certain common characteristics so that many of the factors will appear in each, although the weights given to them may be different in each case. In larger companies, however, where there is considerable variation in the requirements of many of the kinds of positions, it may be necessary to set up separate systems and procedures for factory, clerical, technical, professional and supervisory or administrative work, although the professional, supervisory and administrative activities may be combined into one group, with certain variations.

If job evaluation methods are to include all the four general classes of work, it is good practice to set up four different plans: one for factory work, one for office work, one to cover technical, professional and administrative work, and one to cover supervisory work but to consist of the third plan modified by the addition of one or two job factors specifically applicable to supervisory responsibilities.

Table 8

GENERAL CLASSES OF WORK SUBJECT TO JOB EVALUATIONS METHODS

Shop or Factory Work

    Nature of work predominantly physical.

    Detailed methods and procedures generally established.

    Primarily involves manual or mechanical skills.

General Office Work (Clerical and Interpretive)

    Nature of work predominantly mental.

    Some manual skill involved in operation of office machines and appliances; however, concurrent mental effort involved.

    Usually methods and procedures established in general only, and application is a matter of interpretation as applied to specific tasks.

Technical, Professional and Administrative Work

    Nature of work predominantly mental, usually in a field of endeavor requiring advanced schooling or education, or of a highly confidential and responsible nature associated with the management of the business.

    Usually involves some form of creative effort and the exercise of discretionary judgment entailing considerable responsibility.

Supervisory Work

    Nature of work predominantly mental, primarily concerned with the organization, planning, directing and coordinating of over-all work programs.

    Involves recommending, formulating and/or administering of over-all company policies, regulations or union agreements.

    Involves responsibility for successful performance of management responsibilities in order to permit successful operation of the business.

9. *Methods of making job studies.* The four methods most generally considered for making job studies are outlined in Table 9. The methods calling for questionnaires to employees and questionnaires to supervisors are not recommended. The reason for this is that a per-

son answering such a questionnaire may be biased in the attempt to secure as high a job rating as possible, regardless of the requirements of the particular job held.

The committee or group of supervisors method has the drawback that the members of such a group are not usually in a position to be thoroughly familiar with the details of the work being done. Consequently, they

Table 9

METHODS OF JOB STUDY

Questionnaire to Employee

Each employee asked to describe his job, its operations, duties and responsibilities. Also requested to furnish estimates of educational and experience requirements and amount of judgment and decisions involved.

Questionnaire to Supervisor

Supervisor asked to describe each job in detail, including operations, duties, responsibilities. Also estimate of educational and experience requirements and amount of judgment and decisions involved.

Duties and Responsibilities Prepared by Committee or Group of Supervisors

Committee or group of supervisors prepares a statement of job duties, responsibilities and operations. Estimate educational and experience requirements and amount of judgment and decisions involved.

Observation of Job by Analyst and Discussion of Duties and Responsibilities with Supervisor

Job analyst obtains brief list of duties and responsibilities from supervisor. Actually observes job and obtains "feel" of job requirements by discussion with job encumbent and supervisors. Obtains supervisors' estimate of educational and experience requirements and analysis and judgment required.

Table 10

JOB STUDY CHECK SHEET FOR ASSEMBLING JOB REQUIREMENTS

Occupation_____

Dept._____Location_____

Education

    Specify how the job duties involve factors such as the following:

        Making mathematical calculations.

        Compiling and making reports—preparing memoranda.

        Interpreting drawings, blueprints, specifications, wiring, diagrams, etc.

        Understanding of physical, electrical or chemical formulae.

        Principles of mechanics or electricity.

        Use of measuring and testing instruments.

        Trades, vocational, or apprentice training.

Experience

    Previous related experience required.

    Job training required.

Initiative and Ingenuity

    Job instruction received.

    Job planning required.

    Is work repetitive or diversified?

    Supervision available for assistance.

    Job contacts required (type, kind, etc.).

    Decisions required (type, kind, frequency or affecting quality, quantity, etc.).

    Job set-ups or devising of new methods, tools, etc., required.

    Determination of feeds, speeds, tools, etc.

Physical Demand

    Work positions involved (standing, sitting, stooping, stretching, etc.).

    Objects handled (weight, frequency).

    Work motions involved (kind, duration, frequency).

Mental—Visual Demand

    Describe amount of time and degree of application involved in:

        Automatic operation.

Job Evaluation

   Positioning of parts, tools, materials, etc.
   Working to limits.
   Analysis of operations.

Responsibility for Equipment or Process
   Equipment or process subject to damage.
   Probable damage and cause.
   Cost of each repair or replacement.
   Total amount of any one loss.

Responsibility for Material or Product
   Material or product involved.
   Probable damage and cause.
   Total amount of any one loss before detection.

Responsibility for Safety of Others
   Hazards to others due to their presence in areas where work is being performed; e.g., from faulty handling and placing of materials, fastening of tools or work; falling objects, use of poisons or acids, safeguarding dangerous area, etc.
   Describe extent of injury to others and state amount of time actually spent on work involving hazards to others.

Responsibility for Work of Others
   Describe extent of, and approximate number of employees involved in (1) directing efforts of others, (2) instructing others, (3) maintaining flow of work in group.

Working Conditions
   Describe amount of time and degree to which employee is adversely affected by actual job conditions involving (1) heat, (2) dust, (3) light, (4) cold, (5) vibrations, (6) water, (7) fumes, (8) noise, (9) lubricants, (10) other conditions.

Hazards
   Probable injury to employees presented by duties performed; e.g., handling and placing of materials, fastening tools or work, falling objects, use of poisons, acids, cutting tools, flying chips, scaffolds, high voltages, etc. Indicate when a hazard has been removed by safeguards, and state whether safeguards are foolproof or depend on proper action of employees.
   Describe probable seriousness of injury and state amount of time actually spent on work where hazard is present.

may overrate some jobs and underrate others, thereby laying the ground for later complaints and dissensions.

The fourth method, whereby a special experienced job analyst personally observes jobs and learns about them through careful and pointed questioning of the various job supervisors, is by far the most effective method. It provides the best means for obtaining the most nearly accurate information, preparing the job descriptions, and finally rating the job.

In making a job study, a job study check sheet is of considerable use for assembling and classifying the information. It requires the analyst to review the important requirements of a job according to the individual job factors. It is also of help in later reviewing a job by showing how the job was originally set up. Table 10 provides an illustration of a job study check sheet.

10. *Applying a job evaluation plan.* Based upon the elements and factors already discussed, the job evaluation plan which has been selected and worked out according to constructive practices can be applied. The factor and degree definitions must first be agreed upon by all those who are concerned with the setting up and administering of the plan. Selection should be made of twenty-five to forty key jobs which represent both a cross section of all the jobs to be studied and a group of jobs for which there are already accepted differential values.

These key jobs should then be written up as job grade substantiations specifications covering the duties,

Job Evaluation

Table 11

JOB GRADE SUBSTANTIATING DATA
(Non-supervisory Hourly Rated Jobs)

OCCUPATION TITLE: Assembler, Adjuster, Bench Hand GRADE 10

Job Description:

Assembling and/or adjusting of several parts on a semi-repetitive basis where single or very similar techniques are required; includes wiring of small units having a number of components from detailed verbal instructions. Requires a limited degree of skill and job training of approximately three to six months.

Job Factors Evaluation

	Deg.	Pts.	Substantiation of Factor Rating
EDUCATION	1	14	Requires reading simple data on drawing such as stock lists, and understanding of verbal instructions.
EXPERIENCE	2	44	Requires 3–6 months experience to become familiar with the requirements and methods, and to develop the technique to be able to assemble, adjust, wire units satisfactorily.
INITIATIVE AND INGENUITY	2	28	Requires the ability to perform standardized operations from detailed instructions, and to make minor decisions such as spacing, tension, alignment, and operation and quality of work completed.
PHYSICAL DEMAND	2	20	Sits at bench position assembling, using tools, or handling items of light weight continuously, or average weight occasionally.

Plant Management

	Deg.	Pts.	Substantiation of Factor Rating
MENTAL AND/OR VISUAL DEMAND	3	15	Requires continuous attention to perform assembling, adjusting and testing operations involved.
RESPONSIBILITY FOR EQUIPMENT OR PROCESS	2	10	Damage to hand tools and gages would be negligible. Damage to current flow test set used in adjusting could cause loss that would seldom exceed $25 in any one case.
RESPONSIBILITY FOR SAFETY OF OTHERS	1	5	Involves little probability of injury to others due to the arrangement of work positions, method of operation and equipment used.
RESPONSIBILITY FOR WORK OF OTHERS	1	5	No responsibility for work of others.
WORKING CONDITIONS	2	20	Good shop conditions involving some dirt, fumes or heat, but not to a disagreeable extent.
HAZARDS	2	10	Some probability of minor injuries such as cuts, burns and abrasions from use of screwdrivers, soldering iron, and pliers, and from handling of assemblies.
TOTAL POINTS		176	JOB GRADE 10 SCORE RANGE 162–183

responsibilities and requirements of the jobs and establishing the grade of the job. From job study details and job descriptions, a job evaluation plan can be set

Job Evaluation

up and scoring of jobs can be started. Scoring jobs in terms of 2nd and 3rd degree is not sufficient. Substantiating reasons must be given for the scoring, as shown in Table 11, in order to make possible consistent scoring of individual factors on future jobs evaluated.

A comparison can then be made between the degree and points evaluation of the selected jobs, such as shown in Table 11, and the actual wage rates being paid for these jobs in the company applying the particular plan. A correlation chart can then be drawn to check on the relationships between job values and rates of pay. This will provide the means of making equitable wage rate adjustments in conformity with the job ratings developed through job evaluation.

Review

What is meant by "job evaluation"?

What steps need to be taken in setting up wage and salary plans?

Give a definition of job rating.

What is the purpose of analyzing job requirements?

Name and describe the three general types of job measurement which are in use for evaluating jobs.

What four classes of work may be covered by job evaluation plans, and in what respects may the plans need to be varied in applying them to each class of work?

What four methods are in use for making job studies, and which is the most effective?

CHAPTER XX

Merit Rating

1. *Purpose and objectives of merit rating.* Merit rating plans are used in industry for the purpose of evaluating the qualities and capabilities of individuals in the organization, as a means for placement, training and promotion. If properly carried on, the measuring of the talents and performance of the various persons within the company has several important advantages. Among these are the following:

- (a) It gives opportunity to find out whether the individual is placed in a position where he can do the best in his work.
- (b) It evaluates his potentialities for the proper performance of his work, and his qualifications for advancement.
- (c) It leads to conference with him, whereby his attitudes, reactions, ability to get along with his associates, and his loyalty to the company can be measured.
- (d) It can be combined with counseling, and thus aid him in developing his fundamental abilities.
- (e) It offers opportunities for comparisons of employees, so as to select the apparently most ca-

Merit Rating

pable persons when new jobs are to be filled.

(f) It results in increased production because of the greater interest the person takes in his work.

(g) It demonstrates to employees that the company is interested in them to a greater extent than that of getting more work out of them.

(h) It minimizes bias and prejudice in evaluating employees' potentialities.

(i) It assembles information whereby pay rates can be set more equitably throughout the organization.

2. *Selecting and formulating the rating factors.* The steps taken in developing a rating program, which is usually developed under the auspices of a committee, are as follows:

(a) Develop job specifications.//
(b) State the aims and uses of the supervisory rating plan.//
(c) Work up the rating form, and list the characteristics which are to be measured.//
(d) Develop the rating procedure.//
(e) Decide how to use the results.//
(f) Train the raters.//
(g) Set up an educational program.

The following factors are commonly used in developing job specifications, the latter five being involved in the case of executive or supervisory jobs:

(a) Skill and experience.//
(b) Education and intelligence.

(c) Responsibility.
(d) Mental effort.
(e) Physical effort.
(f) Personality.
(g) Leadership.
(h) Training ability.
(i) Personal productivity.
(j) Productivity of unit.
(k) Personal efficiency.
(l) Efficiency of local department.
(m) Requisites of a special nature.

The rating scale is developed by first deciding which factors or qualities should be included in the analysis procedure, and how these qualities should be stated or defined. Qualities which can be clearly distinguished and specifically designated should be selected; not those which may have ambiguous meanings. Otherwise, serious differences of opinion may arise as to interpretations of the various factors and the assigning of values in the rating scale.

It is not sufficient merely to name, or describe in general, the meaning and nature of the qualities selected for the grading scale. Since the ratings are to be made for serious purposes, to define and distinguish qualities in a fair and equitable manner, it is highly important that each quality be broken down into a number of specifically indicative elements.

Five or more elements should be selected in each case. These elements should be chosen and stated in

Merit Rating

some standard manner, but should be practical and definitive, so that all ratings can be made on as sound and mutually understandable basis as possible.

3. *Evaluating the ratings.* There are several different ways of scoring the merit ratings. One way is by a classification procedure. This method has special advantages in that it is expository and can be blocked out into special classes, rather than recorded on a numerical scale. The qualities to be rated are first decided upon, and are expressed in common interpretive terms such as the following:

- (a) Organizational ability.
- (b) Ability to adopt advanced procedures.
- (c) Assumption of responsibility and exercise of good judgment.
- (d) Reliability and interest in performance of work.
- (e) Cooperative with executives and subordinates.
- (f) Interested in the selection and development of subordinates.
- (g) Capable in analysis of operating problems.
- (h) Loyal to the company and conscientious in his work.
- (i) Able to make decisions.
- (j) Forward-looking; able to sense future developments.

In scoring the merit ratings of employees so as to evaluate the relative capabilities of the various individuals, several methods are used. Two of the simpler methods are the line scale and the profile scale.

The line scale consists of horizontal lines divided off into, say, five equal sections if there are five grades of a characteristic to be check-marked. Five definitive grades of each characteristic are recorded under the five divisions, and the grader puts a check over the division of the lines which correspond to his evaluation of the rated individual's ability in the particular characteristic. This method requires large forms, but it is informative and indicative of the person's capabilities.

The profile scale, a second form, has ten ruled vertical numbered divisions, and a horizontal zero line at the middle, above which are equally-spaced two lines of ticks, the upper two being 1 and 2, the lower two being -1 and -2. On each of the ten vertical lines, the evaluator of the individual places a point at the plus or minus level which expresses his evaluation of the person tested and the specific characteristics. The lines connecting the points give a graph of the evaluation of the employee, thus indicating his gradation.

4. *Other methods of merit rating.* There are other procedures and forms used in connection with merit rating. They include the following:

(a) The graphic rating scale, which is a form listing at the left eight major employee characteristics and their definitions, to the right of which are five columns labeled with an ascending degree of proficiency in each of the characteristics. Checks in the columns enable the grader to indicate his relative opinion of the candidate, un-

Merit Rating

der the proper column, and beside the proper characteristic.

(b) An estimate-of-qualities sheet, with characteristics—in six groups—listed at the left, and five columns at the right for checks in the columns headed: "Outstanding," "Good," etc.

(c) An employee's rating chart, with vertical columns for quality rated, details of quality, spaces in which unsatisfactory, average, and satisfactory positive qualities are checked, and summarized ratings.

(d) A points value sheet listing eleven employment factors, six being at the left to indicate personal factors, and five dealing with operating data.

Review

What is the purpose of merit rating plans?

Name some of the advantages of measuring the talents and performance of employees.

What steps must be taken in developing a rating program?

List the factors commonly used in developing job specifications.

What care should be taken in developing a rating scale?

Name some of the methods used in scoring the merit ratings of employees.

CHAPTER XXI

Personnel Relations

1. *The personnel department.* In most small and medium-size plants, personnel relations and labor relations are administered through an integrated department. Such a department is variously known as the Personnel Department, the Industrial Relations Department, or perhaps a combination of both.

For purposes of the text and in the interest of clarity and better organization, the subject of personnel relations and that of labor relations will be treated in two separate chapters, with this chapter dealing with the former, and the next chapter with the latter. As a matter of fact, as the work becomes increasingly complex, a separation, organization-wise, becomes almost mandatory.

2. *Personnel functions.* The duties of the personnel department consist of planning, setting up, directing and carrying on the functions having to do with the following:

(a) Employment.
(b) Movement of employees within the organization.

Personnel Relations

(c) Wage and salary control.
(d) Training and related activities.
(e) Employee service.
(f) Financial aids.
(g) Fringe benefits.
(h) Safety and accident prevention.
(i) Medical services and industrial hygiene.
(j) Records and follow-up.
(k) Community relations.

3. *Employment.* The vital function of employing personnel must be headed by a well-qualified employment manager with broad knowledge of both the plant and the community. His services are indispensable to the smooth working of the plant. He should have an able staff of interviewers and clerical assistants to help him perform his function by relieving him of a large amount of routine work.

The employment manager usually reports to the personnel manager. The medical director, who is responsible for physical examinations, should not report to the employment manager, although his work is closely coordinated with that of the employment manager. The medical director usually reports to the personnel manager or to some executive higher up in the organization.

In employing personnel, attention has to be given to the following matters:

(a) Labor supply sources.
(b) Labor rate surveys.

- (c) Selection.
    - (1) Application blank—interview—pre-employment tests.
    - (2) Physical examinations.
    - (3) Reference check.
    - (4) Explanation of union working conditions—check-off, union shop, probationary period, seniority system.
    - (5) Job assignment.
- (d) Induction—explanation of company policies, working rules, benefits, introduction to foreman or supervisor.
- (e) Records section—seniority system.

4. *Movement of employees within the organization.* It is the duty of the personnel manager and his top assistants to attend to the movement of employees within the organization, which results from the following:

- (a) Promotions.
- (b) Transfers.
- (c) Layoffs.
- (d) Demotions.
- (e) Discharges and quits.
    - (1) Exit interviews.

The incentive to get ahead must be kept alive through promotions and transfers. Layoffs and demotions, when they occur, must be softened as much as possible. Under some union security contracts where plant-wide seniority exists, the layoff procedure may

Personnel Relations

become a complicated and onerous task for the personnel manager and the labor relations manager, requiring the coordination of both their efforts.

A so-called Disciplinary Control Board has found wide application in industry for the handling of the discharged employee. Such a board, composed of the personnel manager, the plant manager and the superintendent involved in the discharge, acts as a final court of appeal. Under this arrangement, the foreman does not have final power of discharge, but can only send the employee from his department pending a hearing before the Board. In highly unionized companies, such a procedure greatly reduces discharge grievances.

Exit interviews are valuable in learning the source of difficulties in the plant. Every effort should be made to interview each terminating employee to make certain that he leaves with the best possible impression of the company.

5. *Wage and salary control.* One of the plus items forced upon industry during World War II was wage and salary control. The war hastened the acceptance of job analysis, job description, and job evaluation and when peace was declared, industry to a greater extent than ever before embraced the principle of sound control of wages and salaries. This practice, along with merit rating, is the accepted practice of all well-managed factories today. The factors entering into wage and salary control, which have been previously discussed in this text, may be summarized as follows:

(a) Job analysis and evaluation.
(b) Job description.
(c) Wage surveys—community, industry, national.
(d) Evaluation of each job or position to determine the worth of each in relation to the whole wage structure.
(e) Wage ranges and brackets.
(f) Enforcement of government wage and salary controls currently in effect.
(g) Merit rating.
(h) Cost-of-living studies.
(i) Periodic review of employee's earnings.

The unions, in an attempt to get an employee to the top of his wage range, are bringing constant pressure to force automatic progression increases at the end of 60 days, 90 days and 6 months. This plan leaves no room for merit increases. Good wage and salary control will combat such practices, since merit advances are highly desirable, particularly in the case of the better employee.

6. *Training and related activities.* The following outline is typical of the types of training that are in general acceptance throughout industry.

(a) On-the-job training, also "vestibule" schools.
(b) Apprentice training.
(c) Improved methods training.
(d) Training of foremen and minor supervisors.
(e) Executive training.
(f) College recruitment and interviewing.

Personnel Relations

- (g) Cadet training program for college graduates.
- (h) Training in economics and the American system of free enterprise.
- (i) Training in company policies, organization and products.
- (j) Cooperation with safety and medical departments.
  - (1) Safety training.
  - (2) First aid training.
  - (3) Health and preventive medicine training.
- (k) Libraries for special studies.

Of special significance is the renewed emphasis put upon supervisory and executive training. This program ranges from executive training courses of various lengths held at the Harvard Graduate School of Business and the Work Shop Seminar Training Courses of the American Management Association, to a wide variety of courses given in the plant. A general term for such courses is "Management Development." The term is significant in that the line is being drawn more and more clearly between management on the one hand and the union employees on the other.

7. *Employee service.* Employee service consists of providing employees with the following:

- (a) Various types of communication programs:
  - (1) Employee magazine.
  - (2) Bulletin boards.
  - (3) Various types of educational meetings.
- (b) Recreational and athletic activities.

(c) Restaurants, canteens and other forms of food dispensing.
(d) Counseling system for company as well as personal business.
(e) Various types of education, i.e., economics, public speaking, not relating to direct training for the factory.
(f) Visiting nurses (although more frequently listed under the medical department).

In recent years, special emphasis has been placed upon keeping the employee more fully informed with respect to company, civic and national problems. As a result, many companies have initiated so-called "Communication Programs," and have placed much emphasis on courses explaining the American system of competitive enterprise.

8. *Financial aids.* Some form of financial aid should be provided plant employees. Of the various forms, credit unions have a very good record, as have certain mutual savings plans and building and loan associations. Other means which companies have adopted for the purpose of rendering financial aid to their employees are included in the following list:

(a) Credit unions.
(b) Mutual savings plans, building and loan association.
(c) Advances on wages.
(d) Loans to laid-off employees.
(e) Employees' exchange organization.

Personnel Relations

(f) Other forms of financial aid.
  (1) Special discounts on the company's product.
  (2) Workmen's compensation insurance.
  (3) Unemployment insurance.

9. *Fringe benefits.* Fringe benefits is a term commonly used today to denote those benefits over and above the actual wages and salaries paid. In the past, these were given by the company of its own free will; today many of these benefits are tied up with the collective bargaining agreement.

The UAW-CIO, for example, negotiated a 5-year contract with many of the automobile companies providing not only for various forms of hospital and surgical insurance, but also for a rise and fall in the wages according to the Bureau of Labor Statistics cost-of-living index, and an annual improvement factor amounting to four cents per hour per year for the life of the contract.

The most important fringe benefits are the following:

(a) Pension plans.
(b) Group life insurance.
(c) Group hospitalization.
(d) Group surgical insurance.
(e) Employee stock ownership.

10. *Safety and accident prevention.* The important work of safety and accident prevention is frequently

under the direct supervision of the works manager, although the personnel manager, from a human angle, must always maintain an active interest in safety and accident prevention. Proper organization, mechanical aids, education and training—these are the keys to a good safety program. Such programs include the following:

(a) Formulating of safety standards.
(b) Safety education and training.
(c) Mechanical aids.
(d) Safety committee—sometimes jointly with union.
(e) Fire protection.
(f) Plant protection—watchmen, etc.
(g) Safety inspections.
(h) Study to find out causes of accidents.

11. *Medical service and industrial hygiene.* Among the newer developments in the medical service field is the development of X-ray equipment which is cheap and effective enough so that chest X-rays may be taken of each new employee. There is also great emphasis put on periodic physical examinations of supposedly healthy individuals, particularly the junior and senior executives. Many companies have made arrangements with such notable outside medical centers as the Mayo Clinic in St. Paul, Minnesota, the Benjamin Franklin Clinic in Philadelphia, and others, for just that purpose.

Industrial hygiene, or "plant public health," is receiving increasing attention, and many plants employ

Personnel Relations

a full-time industrial hygiene engineer who reports either to the plant medical director or to some higher executive.

The following is a list of services rendered for maintaining employees' health:

(a) Pre-employment physical examination.
(b) Routine medical services, injuries, minor ailments.
(c) Visiting nurses.
(d) Periodic chest X-rays.
(e) Periodic physical examinations for all or part of the organization.
(f) Checkup on plant hygiene and sanitation.

12. *Employee records.* Good, clear-cut records which are readily available and easily understandable are invaluable in personnel and labor relations. Records should be kept in a fireproof vault for a limited number of years, then transferred to microfilm for permanent filing.

The tabulation of various data such as payrolls, seniority lists, vacation lists, pension lists, are handled in modern plants through some form of punch card system. The rapidity with which valuable figures can be made available adds greatly to the smooth functioning of any organization.

Review

What functions are carried on by the personnel department of a plant?

Name some of the duties of the employment manager.

What are the various reasons for the movement of employees within an organization?

What factors enter into wage and salary control?

Name some of the types of training that are provided by industrial organizations.

In what ways does a company render employee service?

What sources of financial aid are available to an employee?

Give examples of fringe benefits.

Name some of the measures taken to prevent accidents.

Through what means does a company endeavor to maintain the health of its employees?

CHAPTER XXII

Labor Relations

1. *Organization of a labor relations department.* Perhaps the best advice that can be given a plant manager with a highly unionized factory is that he hire a thoroughly experienced labor relations manager and have him organize a small, tightly-knit department. The members of this department should devote all their time to working with the union. They should have available either in the company, or as an outside consultant, an attorney well versed in labor union law. The many legal implications arising under the various forms of government wage and salary stabilization controls make mistakes very costly. Hence, sound legal counsel is a "must."

Many plants ranging from 5,000 to 10,000 employees have to deal with two or often three unions. For example, United Auto Workers–CIO may be the bargaining agency for the production workers; the American Federation of Labor union for the patternmakers; and perhaps an independent union for the office workers, engineers, and similar "white collar" or professional groups. Whatever the setup, proper organizational steps must be taken to deal with each union group.

2. *Dealing with unions*. Dealing with unions is an exceedingly complex task that cannot be adequately covered in a single chapter. For purposes of this text, the task may be divided into three principal divisions—

(a) The recognition of the bargaining unit.
(b) The actual negotiations of the union contract.
(c) The day-to-day operation under the contract.

The National Labor Relations Board has developed a set of rules, through a series of cases, which can serve as a guide to prevent any charge of failure to bargain in good faith. It is well to recognize these rules since they will do much to eliminate friction and make for good will in future operations. The guide-posts are as follows:

(a) Union recognition—by consent, by display of signed membership cards, by election; through the National Labor Relations Board.
(b) Reasonable correspondence with reference to setting up time of meetings and maintaining contact with the union.
(c) Conferences with union.
(d) Appointing committees of management duly authorized to negotiate for the company.
(e) Meetings with union negotiators.
(f) Proposals and counterproposals.
(g) Formulation of written agreement—the union contract.

3. *Recognition of bargaining unit*. The plant manager and the labor relations manager must make certain,

Labor Relations

when dealing with unions, that they are bargaining with bonafide representatives of duly authorized unions. If this is not done, the plant may be saddled with a union that does not truly represent the employees. Challenges by rival unions will undoubtedly follow and plant turmoil is inevitable. Never assume that the union seeking to organize the plant represents the majority of the employees; further, never take its word for it.

There is a fixed procedure set up by the National Labor Relations Board for determining first, which union, if any, represents the majority of the employees; and second, the particular group of employees, such as the shop and maintenance group, the electrical workers, the office group, and the engineers, which will comprise the bargaining unit.

For example, the various CIO unions generally try to organize the shop and maintenance workers, while the AFL unions organize the various crafts, such as the bricklayer, the pipefitter, and the electrician crafts. Only in the case of the independent union is the whole plant likely to be covered by one union in a single collective bargaining unit.

4. *Certification, holding elections.* Unionization of a plant begins by a membership drive which is usually evidenced by cards signed by employees designating their preference. These cards are taken to the Labor Board and this Board then decides if sufficient interest exists to warrant an election. Just what measuring stick is used to determine the proper amount of interest is

usually a closely kept secret, but it is generally assumed that if 30 per cent of the number of employees in a particular unit sign up, an election will be held.

Arrangements for the election are held under the supervision of the Labor Board which assigns agents, and permits each party to appoint watchers in the usual political custom. A ballot listing the choices, such as UAW-CIO, independent union, and no union, is printed, and the parties concerned are notified as to polling place and time. A special tabulating run is generally made of the eligible employees, and this list is closely adhered to during the elections. In this way, challenged votes and disputes are greatly reduced.

When the ballots are all counted and the disputes resolved, the Board renders its decision by denying the petition if the vote is negative. Otherwise, the union having the majority of the votes is certified as the exclusive bargaining agent for the plant. Usually, the Board will not permit another election for a year, although the trend toward two- and five-year contracts may extend this period.

Election and certification are not the only ways a union may prove it represents the majority of the employees of a particular plant. If union leaders should offer lists of their dues-paying members to an employee, or offer him a number of application cards, the procedure is to consult the Labor Board as to the best course. The Board may order the employer to deal with the union prior to certification.

Labor Relations

5. *Negotiating the union agreement.* The bargaining unit may be the entire personnel of the plant, including the shop, office, engineering, and other groups. Usually, however, this is not the case. The appropriate unit is generally determined by the Labor Board based on the facts of the case, including tradition, relations between groups of workers, and the wishes of the employees. In any event, the plant manager should make sure that a clearly defined, workable unit is set up.

The certification will include a definition of the bargaining unit, so the next step is to organize for registration. To do this, the plant manager must be sure that the line organization is well represented, since it is these representatives who must operate under the contract. A union agreement which is negotiated by a lawyer or a labor relations manager alone, without a liaison member or the plant manager present, may often be the source of many operating troubles.

A suggested committee is as follows: Labor Relations Manager, Chairman, Assistant Works Manager, or some other duly authorized member of the Plant Manager's office, Assistant Labor Relations Manager, and a contract writer. In most instances, it is best to keep the lawyer out of direct negotiations; he can serve best by drafting in legal language the agreement reached in bargaining. This is not to say that lawyers are not frequently present at bargaining sessions. They should be, but only as advisers rather than direct negotiators.

6. *Contract clauses.* There are many subjects to be covered in a union contract. For purposes of this text, a listing of the principal contract clauses may be considered adequate. Usually, the following clauses are of prime importance:

(a) Prerogatives of management—these are sometimes spelled out in detail, sometimes assumed and not mentioned in contract.
(b) Union recognition and coverage.
(c) Union security.
(d) Grievance procedure.
(e) Wages, hours and working conditions.
(f) Seniority groupings.
(g) Vacations.
(h) Duration of contract.
(i) Arbitration, mediation.
(j) Various other items.

7. *Excerpts from actual union contract.* From a practical point of view, the following excerpts from an actual contract have much to offer by way of illustration:

This agreement, made and entered into this 17th day of July, 1950, by and between the BUDD COMPANY, Philadelphia (Hunting Park Plant), a duly organized corporation doing business in the City of Philadelphia, Pennsylvania, party of the first part, hereinafter designated as the "Company," and the INTERNATIONAL UNION, UNITED AUTOMOBILE, AIRCRAFT AND AGRICULTURAL IMPLEMENT WORKERS OF AMERICA, Affiliated

Labor Relations

with the CIO and Local 813 thereof, parties of the second part, hereinafter called the "Union."

Article I — Recognition and Coverage

Section 1. The Budd Company, Philadelphia Hunting Park Plant, hereby recognizes the International Union, United Automobile, Aircraft and Agricultural Implement Workers of America (UAW-CIO) and Local 813 thereof, as the exclusive bargaining agency with respect to wages, hours, working conditions, dismissals and discriminations for all production and maintenance employees of the Company, including group leaders, matrons, toilet men, expediters, stationary engineers, gas and arc weld school instructors, test department employees, storekeepers, assistant storekeepers, chauffeurs, truck drivers, photographers, and blueprint machine operators; but exclusive of patternmakers, patternmaker apprentices, office and shop clerical employees, personnel interviewers, employment interviewers, and job analysts, rate setters, time-study men, safety inspectors, guards, secretary to the president, secretaries to the vice-presidents, treasurer, comptroller, personnel manager, or secretaries of the Company, assistant foremen and persons of equal or higher rank, and all other supervisory employees with authority to hire, promote, discharge, discipline or otherwise effect changes in the status of employees or effectively recommend such action, and will only negotiate collectively with such representatives of the Union as are duly accredited and chosen by its members for the purpose of determining any disputes which may arise concerning wage rates, working conditions, hours, dismissals, or discriminations, subject to and in accordance with the provisions of the National Labor Relations Act and applicable orders of the National Labor Relations Board.

Section 2. Wherever the word "employee" appears in this agreement it shall only be considered to refer to those employees within the collective bargaining unit designated in Section 1 of this ARTICLE.

Article II — Union Security

Effective as of June 21, 1950, the following sections shall apply:

Section 1. All employees who are presently members of the Union shall remain members of the Union as a condition of employment.

Section 2. All employees who complete their probationary period after June 21, 1950 shall become members of the Union and must remain members of the Union as a condition of employment.

Section 3. The Company and the Union agree to a voluntary deduction of Union dues, assessments and initiation fees for those employees who are members of the Union.

Section 4. The Budd Company will not, in any manner, interfere with the rights of, nor discriminate against any employee because of his membership in the Union, nor will the Company give special privileges to, or bestow any favors upon an employee because of non-membership in the Union.

Article III — Union Representatives

A. SHOP STEWARDS:

Section 1. There shall be one shop steward for each shift in each division or location who shall be selected by the Union from among the employees of that division or location.

Section 2. In the departments of one hundred or more employees, there shall be an additional shop steward for each shift in each division or location for each additional one hundred employees or major fraction thereof if the Union deems this necessary.

Section 3. The shop steward will be permitted to leave his work upon notification to his foreman, for the handling of grievances within the department or departments under his jurisdiction and time so spent will be compensated for by the Company at his average straight time hourly earnings of the previous week providing he has reported to his foreman at the time he leaves his work and upon his return to work. The foreman must sign an allowance slip to be presented to the timekeeper. Any time spent on grievances involving overtime shall be paid for only on approval of the superintendent or Personnel Manager. It is understood that the foreman must release the steward promptly but no steward will leave his place of work until the foreman has placed another man in his position.

Section 4. The Union may designate an alternate steward to each regular steward who shall only function in the absence of the steward. In the event that the steward should be permanently replaced by the alternate steward, the Company shall be notified within 24 hours.

In the event of the absence of the regularly designated steward in any department or departments where no other steward is available, the regularly designated steward shall advise his committeeman and the foreman of the alternate steward who shall function in his absence. The committeeman of such division shall notify the superintendent of such division of this substitution.

B. GENERAL GRIEVANCE COMMITTEE:

Section 5. There shall be a General Grievance Committee of eleven employees plus the President, who shall act as Chairman of the Committee, which shall be the official representatives of the local Union for all of the employees on all shifts dealing with grievances or other matters which go beyond the first step in the grievance procedure. The Union may designate an alternate committeeman to each regular committeeman who shall only function in the absence of the committeeman. In the event that the alternate committeeman should permanently replace the committeeman, the Company shall be notified within 24 hours.

Section 6. Members of the General Grievance Committee shall be permitted to leave their work for the purpose of investigation and adjusting grievances in accordance with the grievance procedure. Time allowance for this purpose shall be paid by the

Company at the employee's average straight time hourly earnings of the previous week providing he has reported to his supervisor at the time he leaves his work and upon his return to work. The foreman must sign an allowance slip to be presented to the timekeeper. Any time spent on grievances involving overtime beyond the allowed one half hour shall be paid for only on approval of the superintendent or Personnel Manager. It is understood that the foreman must release the committeeman promptly but no committeeman will leave his place of work until the foreman has placed another man in his position.

For the purpose of expediting grievances by the committeeman, the committeeman shall be permitted one half hour in addition to his regular working hours in any working day.

Article IV—Grievance Procedure:

Section 1. It is mutually understood and agreed that should any difference arise between the Union, the Company and/or any of its employees as to the meaning and application of any of the provisions of this agreement, or should any local trouble of any kind arise in the Company's Hunting Park Plant, an earnest effort shall be made to settle such differences immediately.

Section 2. The procedural steps for the settlement of grievances hereinafter set forth represent a general standard which may be modified by agreement between the Company and the Union to permit a specific procedure best suited for the orderly and expeditious settlement of grievances provided such modifications are not contrary to the general principles herein established.

Section 3. The procedure under this ARTICLE is available to the Union for the presentation and settlement of grievances arising under the terms of this contract.

Section 4. The General Grievance Committee as described in ARTICLE III, Section 5 hereof, shall operate and be offered such time off as described in ARTICLE III, Sections 5 and 6, as may be required.

(a) To attend regularly scheduled Grievance Committee meetings which shall be held at least once each week during working hours (unless by agreement between the Grievance Committee and Management no meeting is required) and to attend any other meeting of the Grievance Committee called by the Chairman of the Committee or the Committee Union Officer in the absence of the Chairman and upon approval of the Personnel Manager.

(b) To attend special meetings with Company representatives pertaining to discharges or other matters which cannot be reasonably delayed until the time of the next regularly scheduled meeting; and

(c) To visit departments other than their own under their jurisdiction at all reasonable times for the purpose of transacting the legitimate business of the Grievance Committee after notice to the head of the department to be visited and notice to his own immediate supervisor.

(d) The President of the Local Union will be granted access to the Plant upon notification to the Personnel Department.

Section 5. In the settlement of the complaint of an individual and at the individual's own request, the steward in his district through a member of the Union's Grievance Committee, shall have the right to obtain the data concerning the employee's hours, wage rates, piecework or contract rates and service credits from the Personnel Manager's office.

Section 6. The Union agrees, on behalf of its stewards, to treat and keep any such information as confidential and will restrict the use of same to its connection with any proper investigation or prosecution of such employee's complaint. This shall not preclude the use of such information in the prosecution of similar cases.

Section 7. The following shall be the grievance procedure for settling disputes: Step No. 1. All grievances may be referred by an employee to his recognized steward and shall be taken up with his immediate foreman within 48 hours after the grievance arose or became known, in an effort to negotiate a satisfactory solution to said employee's grievance. The foreman shall render his decision within 8 hours after the conclusion of any such negotiations and shall sign the written grievance form which shall be provided by the company for this purpose with his conclusions and recommendations clearly noted thereon. (If the aggrieved employee so desires, he may be present when the steward dis-

cusses his grievance with the immediate foreman.)
Step No. 2. In the event the foreman's decision may be unsatisfactory to the Union, the grievance shall be taken up, within 48 hours after the foreman's decision, by the steward and the grievance committeeman with the superintendent or department head, who shall commence negotiations of the said appealed grievance at once, and he shall render his decision on any such appealed matter within 8 hours, but in no case more than 24 hours, after the conclusion of the presentation of such appealed grievance and shall countersign the written grievance form with his conclusion and recommendations clearly noted thereon. The committeeman may seek the assistance of the chairman of the Grievance Committee in the second step.

Grievances regarding matters of safety may be brought directly into the 3rd step of the grievance procedure.

In cases when necessary, the Personnel Department will call in a Time Study representative to consult with a particular steward and committeeman, and the Personnel Manager, to get all the facts concerning the grievance prior to the third step.

In all cases no more than 32 hours over-all shall be allowed to elapse between the initial presentation of the grievance and the decision of the plant superintendent or department head. If no satisfactory settlement is reached, then: Step No. 3. Any grievance not satisfactorily settled by the superintendent's decision in the second step will be reviewed at the next regular meeting with the Grievance Committee. The General Grievance Committee of the Union shall have the right to further prosecute said complaint at said meeting by negotiations with the appropriate Company representative who shall be promptly designated for such purpose. The decision of the Company Grievance Representative or Representatives must be rendered promptly but in no case delayed beyond 24 hours after the grievance has been discussed. If the decision is still unsatisfactory to the Union, then: Step No. 4. The grievance shall be presented and reviewed at a meeting attended by an International Representative of the Union together with Representatives of the Company and the General Grievance Committee. Such meetings shall be held promptly but in any case not more than one week after the Company decision in the third step, unless such period of time is extended by mutual agreement of the parties. All decisions in the 4th step shall be rendered within three working days of the meeting. If the Management Committee requires additional time to render a decision, the Chairman of the Union Grievance Committee shall be notified.

Step No. 5. The grievance shall not later than 30 days after the rendering of the 4th step grievance answer be submitted for determination by an impartial arbitrator who shall be selected and mutually agreed upon by the Company and the Union. The decision of the arbitrator shall be final and binding upon all the parties, and the expense of the arbitration proceedings, including the compensation paid the arbitrator, shall be shared equally by the Company and the Union.

In the event the Company and the Union cannot agree on an arbitrator they shall ask the American Arbitration Association to name one. This step shall be limited to grievances arising out of violations of the contract or interpretation of same.

Section 8. The Company agrees that neither it nor any of its personnel shall unduly delay the settling of any grievance; however, no grievance which is not normally presented and prosecuted within 30 days of its occurrence shall be recognized.

8. *Arbitration.* It should be noted that when no agreement is reached in the fourth step of the grievance procedure, the Union may take the case to abritration. Arbitration has some advantages; it serves as a face saver and as a safety valve and may help to avoid wild-cat strikes, sitdowns, and walkouts. On the other hand, it is dangerous. No outsiders should make decisions affecting a plant if it can possibly be avoided. Where arbitration functions successfully, it is usually limited to interpretation of the contract. To permit other matters, especially rates of pay and similar vital questions, to be decided by an arbitrator is not good business and it should be resisted to the bitter end.

In some large industries, a permanent arbitrator is included as part of the normal procedure. This means that one man may decide many difficult problems.

Labor Relations

It is the author's belief that regular arbitration through the American Arbitration Association will, in the long run, be more satisfactory from a management point of view, simply because a different arbitrator is assigned to each case by the Association. This is to be desired rather than having a single individual decide a variety of cases.

Review

Into what three divisions may the task of dealing with unions be divided?

State some of the rules which an employer should follow in dealing with employee representatives.

Describe the procedure for determining which union, if any, represents the majority of the employees.

Who should represent management in negotiating with a union?

Name the principal subjects covered in a union contract.

Outline the procedure followed in settling grievances.

Under what conditions is arbitration likely to function successfully?

CHAPTER XXIII

Modern Industrial Trends

1. *The plant manager of today.* The great manufacturing plants which have been developed in modern times provide eloquent testimony to the fact that the plant manager has outgrown the old days when he was simply a grown-up superintendent or a "pusher." The plant manager of today must be a well-educated, broad-minded person who not only understands the operation of a modern industrial plant, but who is also sensitive to the trends of modern industry. There seems to be no better way of concluding this text, therefore, than to summarize briefly some of the present trends in industry.

2. *Productivity approved by labor.* In May 1950, when the United Auto Workers signed their five-year agreement with the General Motors Corporation, it was perhaps the first time in history that a major union openly approved productivity. This contract was epoch-making for several reasons. It was to be in effect for the relatively long period of five years and it included a so-called "Improvement Factor." This meant that the workers were to be awarded with an additional four

cents per hour each year for improvement in production.

The contract also recognized the right of the company to put in technical and other improvements. This seems to have worked out satisfactorily in spite of the fact that the unions demanded an additional one cent per hour in 1953, thus increasing the improvement factor to five cents per hour.

Coupled with this contract was the "escalator clause." This clause provided for a rise and fall in wages in accordance with the variations in the cost of living.

3. *Development of automatic machinery.* One of the interesting developments which resulted from this contract was the fact that the automobile industries really exerted themselves so far as earning the annual improvement factor was concerned. They put great emphasis on automatic machinery and the word "Automation" came into popular usage. There are many examples of such machinery, some of which are described in Chapter XIV.

4. *Increasing use of electronic computers.* The trend towards automation has brought into being more and more scientific methods. Along with automation has come the increasingly wide use of electronic computers and a number of big business firms are equipped with them today. While these devices are frequently referred to as electronic "brains," they are actually tools because they can do only what they are told. Nevertheless, these computers can work amazingly fast; in

some cases, three million times faster than the human mind.

Two basic functions are performed by computers. Measuring is done by the analog computer, just as measuring is done by a speedometer or a water meter. Counting is done by the digital computer which may be likened to an adding machine. These computers have been taken over by industry because, as Vannevar Bush says, "Wherever logical processes of thought are employed—that is, wherever thought for a time runs along accepted grooves—there is an opportunity for the machine."

Computers received a big boost from World War II, although they were originally used for scientific research. During the war, they aided in solving complex problems in the building of the atomic bomb. While devices such as the photo-electric cell, which receives information and feeds controlled power to operate machines, are used primarily in the factory itself, electronic computers in business are used largely for speeding office work. In 1955, large firms were ordering electronic computers at eight times the rate they were ordering them in 1952.

In business organizations, computers have been demonstrably successful in customer billing, in the arrangement of production schedules, and in maintaining control of inventories. They are primarily used in the offices of large insurance firms, utilities, railroads and the aircraft industry.

Modern Industrial Trends

For example, the Southern Pacific Railroad spent $4,000,000 on a dispatching system, ninety-five miles long, in California and Oregon. Here an operator can push a button, and a gas burner will light up under a switch some two-hundred miles distant to prevent it from freezing. One of the big airlines (American) makes use of a computer that will instantly show a record of all seats available on one-thousand of its scheduled flights. Computers are in widespread use by military and naval scientists and researchers, but their most spectacular public demonstrations have been to add up national election figures with lightning-like speed.

5. *Need for technically trained people.* The high initial cost of installing electronic computers is considered to be more than offset by the lowered costs that result from their use. The computers can be purchased outright from their manufacturers or they can be rented. As the use of computers increase in industry, an increased supply of technically trained people will be required to run them and service them.

Just as automation will require increasing emphasis on the brains, rather than the brawn, of the industrial workers, so, too, will the electronic computers require a higher level of technical proficiency of the business employee. Because of this definite need in the future, schools and colleges will have to lay more stress on electrical, mathematical and mechanical sciences in curricula designed for automation and the computer.

6. *Mergers and consolidation.* The plant manager of today cannot overlook the growing tendency towards mergers and consolidations. The automobile industry is one of the best illustrations of this trend.

The independent automobile companies have not been able to survive as such because of the decline in their business to a profitless level. Hence, there has occurred the mergers of Packard and Studebaker, and of Nash and Hudson. Whether these two mergers can survive is still a question. Perhaps eventually they will all combine into what might be a big fourth corporation in the automobile industry, comparing with General Motors, Ford and Chrysler.

7. *The trend toward diversification.* There is also a definite trend at the present time towards more diversification. Large and medium-sized companies are forming subsidiaries which will bring diversification into the picture. Automobile companies are branching out into plastics, into railway car work, and into other fields that bring a wider diversification of their products.

8. *The prospect for guaranteed employment.* Another movement which is now plainly in evidence is that toward so-called "guaranteed employment." Just what will come out of this trend is difficult to say, but there is a tendency toward paying the factory worker on a basis which will give him some form of guarantee for more than his daily wage. Perhaps this will be a guaranteed weekly plan with supplemental income from the Unemployment Compensation Bureau.

Modern Industrial Trends

Right now, Walter Reuther of the United Auto Workers is making a very definite drive for the guaranteed employment plan. What his negotiations with the "Big Three" of the automotive industry will produce cannot be told at this time, but the trend is very definitely there toward some form of guaranteed employment plan.

9. *Emphasis being placed on executive development.* In addition to the trends already mentioned, greater emphasis is now being placed on better executive development. This, together with the maintenance of executive health, is one of the major problems of operating a factory.

In any plant today, there is, on the one hand, the management group which is definitely under the top management direction and, on the other hand, the union group which has an organization of its own. The plant manager must take a very active part in selecting, training and keeping fit his executive staff.

10. *Development of the techniques of operations research.* The plant manager today, to a much greater extent than formerly, must have a good understanding of mathematics because of the definite trend towards more refined mathematical calculations. As management and executive problems increase with the growing complexities of modern industry and business, top level management is turning to practical, workable mathematical techniques as an aid in difficult decision-making functions.

One of these techniques is "linear programming," an approach which is aimed at reducing judgment questions to problems of calculation. While this may be an over-simplification, linear programming has been found effective in determining the most desirable or profitable course of managerial action in situations affected by a number of variables and conditions. It allows management to decide upon a wise answer, arrived at mathematically, from several alternatives.

Used properly by those familiar with its scope, linear programming can be applied successfully in reaching decisions regarding product mix, machine scheduling, warehouse location, inventory control and executive salary evaluation. In one particular case, a firm found that it took the guesswork out of the decision of whether they should manufacture their product at its point of use or should ship to distant points. Linear programming proved that the latter course was the better and experience justified its findings.

Other modern scientific techniques are often used in conjunction with linear programming. Such programs as methods engineering, which is the technical evaluation of the effectiveness of methods or procedures, and methods-time-measurement studies, a scientific time evaluation of manual operation, have been brought into play by modern industrialists to help solve their problems.

All of these techniques are part of what may be referred to as "operations research," a form of searching study upon which sound executive decisions may be based. Operations research was used successfully to plan the great invasion over the Normandy beaches during World War II. Translated to business and industry, operations research may be used to supply answers to such questions as what will be needed if a firm is to introduce a new product capable of competing successfully with established brand names already on the market.

Operations research uses the scientific approach, coupled with such devices as the electronic computer, to replace "guess-timates" with tested, workable figures. In one example, which may be extreme, operations research techniques showed one firm that it was actually more profitable to produce at *less* than full capacity, a conclusion that was impossible to arrive at through managerial judgment alone, no matter how experienced.

The entire field of mathematical techniques today is, in the opinion of Robert O. Ferguson, of Methods Engineering Council, "one step along the road to making management more of a science and less of an art."

Review

What qualifications must the modern plant manager have?

Why may the agreement signed in May 1950 by the United Auto Workers with the General Motors Corporation be considered epoch-making?

Name two basic functions which can be performed by electronic computers, and give examples of the value of such computers to industry.

Why and how will schools and colleges have to revise their curricula because of automation and the electronic computer?

Give an example of the trend toward mergers.

How are companies bringing diversification into the picture?

What is meant by "guaranteed employment"?

Of what value is linear programming?

Give an example of the successful use of operations research techniques.

Index

A

Accident prevention methods, 341–342
Aggregation or accretion, expansion by, 39, 42
Air conditioning:
 advantages of, 196–197
 in plant buildings, 196
Alford, L. P., on production control, 123
American Standards Association and simplification movement, 87
Analog computer, 364
Annual wage plans, 304–306
Arbitration:
 advantages of, 360–361
 procedure in settling grievances, 360
Automatic factory, 241–243
Automatic machinery:
 development of, 363
 types in use, 233–236
Automation:
 and tooling, 228–243
 definition, 236
 in automotive field, 236
 "programming," 236–241
 trend toward, 363–365
 ultimate aim of, 241–243

B

Balance-of-stores sheet, 157
Bargaining unit, recognition of, 346–347, 349
Bedaux Point Wage plan, 302
Bonus plans:
 quality, 302
 waste-elimination, 303
Building maintenance, 285–287

C

Capital, a factor in plant location, 55–56
Chain combinations, 39–40, 47–48
Charts, organization, 112
Circular form of expansion, 39, 46–47
Classification procedure, a method of scoring merit ratings, 331–332
Climate, a factor in plant location, 53–54
Committees:
 advantages and disadvantages of, 96
 equipment, 97–98
 executive, 96–97
 materials-handling, 211
 principles of, 98–99
 production, 98–99
 use of in organization, 95
Complementary form of expansion, 39
Conference:
 need for, 9, 13
 techniques of, 8–9
Consolidation (*See* Mergers)
Continuous method of timing, 251–252, 253–255
Continuous-process industry:
 factory layout in, 184
 production control in, 123–124
 storeskeeping in, 155–156
Control:
 line and staff, 89–101
 of production, 123
 of quality, 162–163
Control chart:
 purpose of, 174–177
 use of, 177

Index

Cost estimating, 274–275 (*See also* Job estimating)
Cost-of-living index wage plan, 304
Cross relationships (*See* Line relationships)

D

Day-work (*See* Wage payment plans)
Day-wage plan:
    advantages of, 298–299
    disadvantages of, 299
    illustration of, 298
Decentralization:
    advantages to employer and employee, 59
    types of, 58–59
Defective materials costs, 278–279
Depreciation costs, 279
Digital computer, 364
Disciplinarian, duties of, 32, 34
Disciplinary Control Board, 337
Dispatch boards, 138–139
Dispatch clerk, duties of, 138–141
Dispatching of work, 124–125, 138–142 (*See also* Production control)
Diversification, trend toward, 366
Documents, written or printed:
    administrative reports, 117
    as mechanisms coordinating executive control, 111–112
    orders and reports, 116, 125–134
    records of performance, 116
    standard-practice instructions, 115–116
Drawing board layouts, 192

E

Electrical equipment, maintenance of, 287
Electronic computers:
    basic function of, 364
    increasing use of, 363–365
    need for technically trained people, 365

Emerson efficiency plan, 302
Employees:
    financial aid available to, 340–341
    fringe benefits to, 341
    medical service and industrial hygiene for, 342–343
    movement of, within organization, 336
    records, 343
    safety and accident prevention programs, 341–342
    service rendered by a company, 339–340
Employment manager, duties of, 335–336
Engineering:
    basic conception of, 219
    department in plant layout, 186
    design, 129, 130, 220–221, 229–230
    division, in production control, 129
    functions of department of, 150, 217–218, 220–221
    importance of methods, 219–220
    improvements of products, importance of, 218–219
    installation of equipment, 224
    methods of, in plant construction, 180
    testing, 223–224
    tooling for production, 222–223
    supplying data to manufacturing departments, 224–226
    use of color in design, 221–222
    use of new methods and equipment, 226
Engineering department, functions of, 150, 217–218, 219, 220–221, 224–226 (*See also* Engineering)
Equipment:
    a factor in materials handling, 201

Index

Equipment (*continued*)
  improvement of materials-handling, 218–219
  installation of, 201, 224
  kinds of materials-handling, 204–209
  reasons for using materials-handling, 202–203
  rules for materials-handling, 199–201
  selection of in plant layout, 184, 186
Escalator clause, 363
Executive:
  control through coordination, 111–112
  duties and responsibilities of top, 12–13
  management, level of authority, 105, 106, 107
  qualifications of an, 1–3
  trend toward development of better, 369
Executives:
  factors in selection of, 7–8
  financial incentives for, 306–307

F

Factor comparison system:
  definition, 313
  procedure followed in, 314–315
Factor point scoring system:
  definition, 313
  procedure followed in, 315–318
Factory buildings:
  methods of planning and constructing, 180
  selection of suitable, 179 (*See also* Plant layout and Plant buildings)
Factory illumination in plant layout, 197
Factory system:
  origin of, 24
  rapid growth of, 27
  social effects of, 25–27
Financial incentive plans for supervisors and executives, 306–307 (*See also* Wage payment plans)
Finished-parts storeroom, operating the, 158–159
Finished-stock record, 159
Fire protection in plant layout, 197
Flow diagrams, 182, 183, 184
Foremanship, functional:
  modern influence of, 32–34
  Taylor's system of, 31–32
Fork trucks, 204–205, 207, 208
Formulas, use of in setting standard time, 265
Frequency distribution, 165, 170 (*See also* Piece-to-piece variation)
Fringe benefits, 341
Functional staff relationships, 108–109, 111

G

Gang boss, duties of, 32, 34
Gantt charts, 137, 138
Gantt task and bonus plan, 302
General staff relationships, 109, 111
Gilbreth, Frank B.:
  founder of motion economy, 267–268
  laws of motion evolved by, 270
  micromotion methods of, 268–269
  therbligs, or elements of motion, 269
Group wage plan, 302
Guaranteed employment, movement toward, 366–367

H

Halsey premium plan, 302
Heating systems for plant buildings, 195–196
Heating, ventilating and plumbing maintenance, 288
Holding-company method of combination, 48

Index

Horizontal combinations, 39, 42–44

I

Improvement factor, 362
Industrial management, leaders of, 36
Industrial relations department (*See* Personnel department)
Industrial Revolution:
  in the United States, 27
  invention of spinning machines, 21–24
  origin, 20
  other inventions, 24–25
  social effects of, 25–27
Industrial-truck handling, 206–209
Inspection:
  and quality control (*See* Statistical quality control)
  cost, a factor in job estimating, 276
  department, function of, 153
Inspector, duties of, 32, 34
Installation of equipment, 224
Instruction-card clerk, duties of, 32, 34
Instruction cards:
  for operators, 130, 141
  procedure in compiling, 262–263
Interchangeability, 82–83 (*See also* Standardization)
Inventories:
  continuous or perpetual, 158
  physical, 160 (*See also* Stores and stocks)

J

Job analysis, definition, 245
Job classification (*See* Job ranking plan)
Job estimating:
  cost factors in, 275–280
  procedures in, 280–281
  reasons for, 273–274
  standards for, 281–282
Job evaluation:
  applying a plan for, 324–327

Job evaluation (*continued*)
  classes of work covered by, 318–320
  definition, 311
  methods of making job studies in, 320–324
  purpose of, 311
  setting up wage and salary plans, 311–313
  types of job measurement in use for, 313–318
Job ranking plan:
  definition, 313
  method of rating by, 314
Job rating, meaning of, 313
Job studies, methods of making, 320–324

K

Kolect-A-Matic pocket, 232

L

Labor:
  a cost factor in job estimating, 276
  productivity approved by, 362–363
  supply in plant location, 54–55
  unrest, a factor in plant location, 60–61
Labor, division of:
  and specialization, 71
  definition, 71, 74–76
  forms of, 74–77
  law of increasing productivity, 80–81
  relationship between quantity, transfer of skill and, 77–81
Labor relations:
  contract clauses in a union contract, 350
  dealing with unions, 346
  negotiating the union agreement, 349
  organization of department of, 345
  recognition of bargaining unit, 346–347

Index 375

Labor relations (*continued*)
responsibility of plant manager, 15–16
unionization of plant, procedure of, 347–348
Labor relations department:
dealing with unions, 346–350
organization of a, 345
Labor relations manager, in dealing with unions, 345–347
Labor unions:
and wage and salary control, 338 (*See also* Labor relations)
attitude toward modern piecerate wage plans, 307–308
result of Industrial Revolution, 26
unionization of plant, procedure of, 347–348
Lateral relationships, 108, 109
Layout of plant (*See* Plant layout)
Leadership:
chief characteristics of, 16
qualities of, 17
Leveling factor:
how to determine a, 260–261
object of motion and time study, 255
rating for skill and effort, 255–260
synthetic method, 261–262
Lift truck, 204–206
Lighting maintenance, 288
Line and staff organization:
advantages and disadvantages of, 94–95
importance of, 93, 95
Linear programming, 368
Line organization:
advantages and disadvantages of, 92–93
chart, 91
duties of foreman under, 92
nature of, 89
works manager's duty under, 92
Line relationships, 108, 109

Line scale method of scoring merit ratings, 332
Lot repetitive industry, production control in, 123
Lot sampling in quality control, 171–174

M

Machines:
automatic, 233–236
breakdowns and repairs in product layout of, 194–195
expansion in the U. S., 27–29
in product layout of, 190–191
methods of arrangement in plant layout, 186–187
Maintenance:
building, 285–287
definition of, 283–284
difference between repairs and, 283–284
heating, ventilating and plumbing, 288
lighting, 288
manufacturing equipment, 287
materials-handling equipment, 288–289
of electrical equipment, 287
of painting work, 289–290
plant-yard, 290–291
power plant, 287–288
preventive, 283
records, purpose and advantages of, 292–293
service installation, 289
service, set-up of, 291
storeroom for equipment and supplies, 291, 292
Maintenance department:
organization of, 284, 291
work done by, 210, 284–285
Maintenance-of-equipment costs, 279
Management:
art of good, 9
independent of top executive, 10
levels of, 105
organization in materials-handling, 211–214

Manuals, organization, 112
Manufacturing:
  equipment, maintenance of, 287
  principles in modern, 71
  specialization in, 72 (*See also* Specialization)
Marstochron, 250
Mass production:
  principles of, 71–87
  product layout in, 187, 188, 190–192
Materials:
  a cost factor in job estimating, 276
  classes of factory, 157
  issue slips, 133, 142, 156
  maximum and maintenance limits for storing of, 157
  ordering for production, 155–156
  procedure in issuing and accounting for, 132–134
Materials handling:
  a cost factor in job estimating, 277–278
  activities involved in, 209–211
  economies of efficient, 202–203
  equipment, maintenance of, 288–289
  high cost of, 199
  kind of equipment used in, 204–209
  major factors in, 201
  methods of, 203–206
  organization for management of, 211–214
  organization of, in small plants, 214–215
  rules of efficient, 199–201
Materials-handling engineer:
  place in organization, 211–212
  responsibilities of, 213
Medical service and industrial hygiene, 342–343
Mergers:
  in automobile industry, 366
  trends in, 40, 366
Merit rating:
  advantages of, 328–329

Merit rating (*continued*)
  factors used in developing job specifications in, 329–330
  methods of scoring, 331–333
  purposes and objectives of, 328–329
  steps in developing a program of, 329
Methods engineer, duties of, 219–220
Methods engineering, 219–220, 368
Methods section of production planning and control department, 128–129, 130, 132
Methods-Time-Measurement method, 271–272, 368
Micromotion method in motion and time study, 248, 268–269
Mnemonic system, 157
Modern industrial trends, 362–369
Modern piece-rate plan, 302–303
Morale, factors which stimulate, 17–18
Motion and time study:
  analyzing the job, 249–250
  definitions of, 245
  factors to be considered in, 246–247
  fatigue, a factor in, 267
  formulas, 265
  Gilbreth, Frank B. and, 267–270
  in production control procedure, 130
  instruction cards, 262–263
  leveling factor, 255–262
  making time studies, 250–255
  methods in general use, 248
  Method-Time-Measurement method, 271, 272
  micromotion methods, 268–269
  motion economy, 267–268
  purposes of, 246
  ratio-delay study method, 265–267
  synthetic method of setting times, 263–265

Index

Motion economy, purpose of, 267–268
Move man, 140, 141, 142
Multiple management:
  as developed by McCormick & Co., 99–100
  structure of, 99–100

N

National Labor Relations Board:
  procedure set up by, 347–348, 349
  rules developed by, 346

O

100 per cent premium plan (*See* Standard hour wage plan)
Operation sheets, 131, 138–139, 141, 142, 225
Operations research, scientific techniques of, 367–369
Orders:
  and reports, difference between, 116
  handling sales, 125, 127–128
Organization, business:
  advantages of large, 40–42
  classifying of activities and assignment of duties in a, 106–108
  committee system in large, 95–99
  defining positions in a, 13–15
  developing a, 10–12
  importance of smaller, 49
  levels of authority in, 105–106
  line, 89–93
  line and staff, 93–95
  methods for measuring size of, 38
  modern trends in, 100–101
  movement of employees in, 336
  movement toward decentralization of, 37–38
  multiple management in, 99–100
  practices of, 102–103
  principles of, 103–105
  relationships in a, 108–112
  trend toward large, 37

Organization (*continued*)
  ways of expanding, 39–40, 42–48
Organization principles, 103–105

P

Painting-maintenance work, 289–290
Pallet method of moving materials, 207–208, 209
Personnel department, duties of, 334–335
Personnel manager, duties of, 335–336
Personnel relations, 334–343
Piece-rate plan:
  advantages and disadvantages of old method, 301
  advantages of hourly guarantee or modern, 302–303
  definition, 298
  difficulties under old method of, 299–300
  modern plan, 302
  old method, 299
  unions attitude toward modern, 307–308
Piece-to-piece variation:
  grouped according to, 163–169
  of parts, 163
Piecework (*See* Piece-rate plan)
Planning boards, 138–139
Planning department in plant layout, 186
Planning, seasoned, 8
Planning section of production planing and control department, 128–129, 132, 133
Plant buildings:
  air conditioning, 196–197
  factory illumination, 197
  fire protection, 197
  heating and ventilating systems, 195–196
  methods of planning and constructing, 180
  use of process flow charts, 180–181 (*See also* Plant layout)
Plant layout:
  air conditioning, 196–197

Plant layout (*continued*)
  analysis of product, 186
  drawing board layouts, 192, 194
  factors to consider in basic layout, 184–185
  factory illumination, 197
  fire protection, 197
  fundamental factors in, 182
  heating and ventilating, 195–196
  machine breakdowns and repairs, 194–195
  methods of machine arrangement, 186–187
  methods of planning, 180
  process flow charts, 180–182
  process layout, 187–188
  product layout, 188, 190–192
  selection of equipment, 186
  template method, 192–194
Plant location:
  availability of water power, 52–53
  capital as a factor in, 55–56
  cost comparisons as a method of, 65–68
  effect of modern influences on, 56
  factors determining, 51–69
  factors to consider in selecting territory, community and site, 61–65
  favorable climate, 53–54
  labor supply, 54–55
  labor unrest, a factor in, 60
  nearness to raw materials, 51–52
  product to be considered, 61
  relocation of, as a defense measure, 56–58, 68–69
  size and selection of community, 62–63
Plant maintenance, 283–310 (*See also* Maintenance)
Plant manager:
  backing up associates, 12
  functions of, 1–18
  fundamental job of, 1
  goals of, 3–6

Plant manager (*continued*)
  in materials-handling management, 211–214
  qualifications of modern, 362
  responsibility for labor relations, 15–16
Plant-overhead costs, 278
Plant relocations:
  as a defense measure, 57, 68–69
  factors determining, 56–57
  reasons for, 57–58 (*See also* Plant locations)
Plant-yard maintenance, 290–291
Policies, formulation of, 6–7
Policy management, level of authority, 105, 107
Power plant maintenance, 287–288
Process flow charts:
  differs from flow diagrams, 182
  use of, 180–181
Process layout, 187–188, 189, 194
Product:
  analysis of, in plant layout, 186
  factors to be considered before plant site selection, 61
Product design:
  for sales appeal, 221–222
  importance of improving, 218–219
  in tooling, 229–230, 231–232
  tie-in with manufacturing processes, 220, 221
Production:
  ordering materials for, 155–156
  planning and control department, 128–129
  putting order into, 128
  tooling for, 222–223
  typical control procedure, 128–132
Production control:
  management's aim, 123
  mechanisms used for, 137–138
  need for planning, 124
  routing, scheduling and dispatching, 124–125, 134–137, 138–142
  typical procedure of, 128–137

Index

Productivity:
  approved by labor, 362–363
  law of increasing, 80–81
Product layout, 188, 190–192, 193, 194–195
Products, improvement of, 218–219
Profile scale method of scoring merit ratings, 332
Profit-sharing plans, 304, 306–307
Purchasing:
  advantages of centralized over localized, 145–146
  economies possible through specifications, 151–152
  importance of specifications in, 150–151
  its place in industry, 144
  legal factors, 145
  policies, 144–145
  receiving and inspecting purchases, 153
  records of information in, 152–153
Purchasing agent:
  duties of, 147–148
  importance of position, 144, 146–147
Purchasing department:
  centralized vs. localized, 145–146
  place in organization, 146–147
  responsibilities of, 148–149

Q

Quality bonus plan, 302
Quality control, 162–178 (*See also* Statistical quality control*)

R

Ratio-delay study in time studies, 265–267
Raw materials, nearness to, a factor in plant location, 51–52
Receiving department, functions of, 153
Records:
  employee, in personnel and labor relations, 343
  finished-stock, 159
  of performance, 116
  purchase, 152–153
  stores and stock, 158
Relationships:
  functional staff, 111
  general staff, 111
  in organization, 108–109
  lateral or cross, 109–110
  line, 109
Repair boss, duties of, 32, 34
Repairs:
  definition of, 284
  difference between maintenance and, 283–284
Reports:
  administrative, 117
  and orders, difference between, 116
Requisitions:
  from several sources, 150–151
  purchase, 149–150
Route clerk, duties of, 32, 34
Route sheets (*See* Operation sheets)
Routing, in production control, 124–125, 134–137 (*See also* Production control)
Rowan wage payment plan, 302

S

Safety and accident prevention programs, 341–342
Salary incentive system (*See* Wage payment plans)
Sales order, handling a, 125, 127
Scheduling of production, 124–125, 134–137 (*See also* Production control)
Scientific management:
  advent of, 29–31
  Taylor's contribution, 31
Scientific techniques in modern industry, 367–369
Service-installation maintenance, 289

Simplification, trend of, 87
Slater, Samuel, father of American manufacturers, 27
Small chance variations, 168
Snap-back method of time study, 251–252
Span of control, 104, 120
Specialization:
  advantages of, 74
  and division of labor, 71, 74–77
  definition, 71–72
  geographical, 72–73
  in manufacturing, 72
  in marketing, 73
  of callings, 73
Specifications:
  economies possible by use of, in purchasing, 151–152
  importance in purchasing, 150–151
Speed boss, duties of, 32, 34
Speedometer, 364
Staff officers, functions of, 93–94
Standard hour wage plan, 302
Standardization:
  advantages and disadvantages of, 86–87
  beginning of, 71
  definition, 81–82
  interchangeability, inspection and, 83
  technical aspects of, 83 (*See also* Standards)
Standard practice instructions, 112, 115–116
Standards:
  international, 83
  marketing, 82
  national, 83–84
  within a factory, 84–86
  within an industry, 84 (*See also* Standardization)
Statistical quality control:
  chart, 164, 165
  departure from pattern, 170–171
  frequency distribution, 165
  lot sampling, 171–174
  meaning of, 162–163

Statistical quality control (*cont.*)
  piece-to-piece variation of parts, 163
  scientific basis of, 169–170
Stop-watch method in motion and time study, 248
Storage-of-materials costs, 279
Storerooms and stock rooms:
  finished-parts storeroom, 158–159
  functions of, 156–157
  necessity for, 154–155
  symbols for, 157 (*See also* Mnemonic system)
Stores and stocks:
  continuous or perpetual inventories, 158
  distinction between, 153–154
  finished-stock record, 159
  maximum and minimum limits, 157
  methods of regulating, 156–157
  operating the finished-parts storeroom, 158–159
  ordering materials for production, 155–156
  physical inventories, 160
Stores-issue slips in production control, 133
Stores-records section:
  clerk, duties of, 133, 140
  in production control, 133–134
  storeskeeper, duties of, 133–134
Supervision costs, 276
Supervisors, financial incentives for, 306–307
Supervisory management, level of authority, 105, 106, 107
Synthetic method of setting times, 263–265

T

Taylor differential piece-rate plan, 302
Taylor, Frederick W.:
  a leader of industrial management, 36

Index

Taylor (*continued*)
  "Art of Cutting Metals," 34
  his procedures and techniques, 35–36, 263–264
  on functional foremanship, 31-34
  on scientific management, 29–31
  on wage studies, 295–296
Template method in plant layout, 192, 194
Testing in engineering, 223–224
Therbligs, 269–270
Time cards, 130, 141, 142
Time studies:
  equipment for making, 250
  fatigue, a factor in, 267
  leveling and rating, 261–262
  procedure followed by time-study man, 251
  ratio-delay study method in, 265–267 (*See also* Motion and time study)
Time study (*See* Motion and time study)
Time-study analyst:
  duties of, 248–249
  procedure followed in time studies, 251
Tool control, 232
Tooling:
  and automation, 228–243
  controlling issue and use of tools, 232
  definitions of different tools, 228–229
  determining tool requirements, 229–230
  for production, 222–223
  where tools are designed, 231
Top management (*See* Policy management)
Training, types provided by organizations, 338–339

U

Union agreement:
  contract clauses in, 350
  excerpts from actual, 350–360
  negotiating the, 349

Use-of-equipment costs, 276–277

V

Ventilating systems for plant buildings, 195–196
Vertical combination or integration, 39, 44, 46

W

Wage and salary control, factors entering into, 337–338
Wage and salary plans, steps in setting up, 311–313 (*See also* Job evaluation)
Wage control system (*See* Wage payment plans)
Wage incentive plans:
  check list for testing effectiveness of, 309–310
  reasons for failure of, 308–309
Wage payment plans:
  advantages and disadvantages of day-wage plan, 298–299
  advantages and disadvantages of old piecework system, 301
  daywork and piecework defined, 297–298
  difficulties under old piece-rate system, 299–300
  essentials of successful, 296–297
  financial incentive for supervisors and executives, 306–307
  legislation affecting administration of, 307–308
  modern wage systems, 301–302
  other wage plans, 303–304
  piecework, old method, 299
  principles based upon, 295
  profit sharing plans, 304, 306–307
  quality bonus plan, 302
  waste-elimination bonus plan, 303
Waste-elimination bonus plan, 303
Water power, a factor in plant location, 52–53

Work orders, handling of, 134–142
Works instruction sheet (*See* Standard practice instructions)
Works manager:
  activities of, 118

Work manager (*continued*)
  as coordinator of plant functions, 117, 118, 119–120
  duties of the, 112–115, 117
  duty under line organization, 92
  on executive committee, 96